C O U N T R Y
Pubs & Inns of
CORNWALL

By Peter Long

Regional Hidden Places

Cornwall
Devon
Dorset, Hants & Isle of Wight
East Anglia
Gloucs, Wiltshire & Somerset
Heart of England
Hereford, Worcs & Shropshire
Lake District & Cumbria
Lancashire & Cheshire
Northumberland & Durham
Peak District
Sussex
Yorkshire

National Hidden Places

England
Ireland
Scotland
Wales

Hidden Inns

East Anglia
Heart of England
North of England
South
South East
West Country
Yorkshire

Country Pubs & Inns

Cornwall
Devon
Sussex
Wales

Country Living
Rural Guides

East Anglia
Heart of England
Ireland
North East of England
North West of England
Scotland
South
South East
Wales
West Country

Published by: Travel Publishing Ltd, 7a Apollo House, Calleva Park, Aldermaston, Berkshire RG7 8TN

ISBN 1-904-43435-5

© Travel Publishing Ltd

Published 2005

Printing by: Scotprint, Haddington

Maps by: © Maps in Minutes ™ (2005)
© Crown Copyright, Ordnance Survey 2005

Editor: Peter Long

Cover Design: Lines and Words, Aldermaston, Berkshire

Cover Photograph: The Weary Friar, Pillaton, Saltash

Text Photographs: © www.britainonview.com

Foreword

The *Country Pubs & Inns of Cornwall* is one of a series of guides which will eventually cover the whole of the UK. This guide provides details of pubs and inns (including hotels which welcome non-residents) situated in the countryside of Cornwall. "Countryside" is officially defined by *The Office of National Statistics* as "settlements of less than 10,000 inhabitants".

There are of course many selectively-based pub guides covering the UK but each title in the Country Pubs & Inns series will provide the reader with the *most comprehensive* choice of pubs and inns in the countryside through handy-sized, county-based guides. The guide enables the reader to choose the pub or inn to visit based on his/her own criteria such as location, real ales served, food, entertainment etc.

This easy-to-use guide is divided into 8 chapters which allows the reader to select the area of Cornwall being visited. Each chapter begins with a map containing the numbered location of the pub or inn and a brief illustrated summary of the places of interest in the area. By using the number the reader can then find more information on their choice of pub or inn.

We do hope that you will enjoy visiting the pubs and inns contained in this guide. We are always interested in what our readers think of the pubs and inns covered (or not covered) in our guides so please do not hesitate to write to us using the reader reaction forms provided to the rear of the guide. Equally, you may contact us via our email address at info@travelpublishing.co.uk. This is a vital way of ensuring that we continue to provide a comprehensive list of pubs and inns to our readers.

Finally, if you are seeking visitor information on Cornwall or any other part of the British Isles we would like to refer you to the full list of Travel Publishing guides to be found at the rear of the book. You may also find more information about any of our titles on our website at www.travelpublishing.co.uk

Travel Publishing

How to use the guide

The *Country Pubs & Inns of Cornwall* provides details of pubs and inns (including hotels which welcome non-residents) situated in the countryside of Cornwall. "Countryside" is defined by *The Office of National Statistics* as "settlements of less than 10,000 inhabitants" so the majority of Cornwall fulfills this definition!

This guide has been specifically designed as an easy-to-use guide so there is no need for complicated instructions. However the reader may find the following guidelines helpful in identifying the name, address, telephone number and facilities of the pub or inn.

Finding Pubs or Inns in a Selected Location

The guide is divided into eight chapters (or sections) each covering a specific geographical area of Cornwall. Identify the area and page number you require from the map and table of contents on the following pages and turn to the relevant chosen page.

At the beginning of each chapter there is a detailed map of the area selected. The villages and towns denoted by *red* circles are places of interest on which information is provided in the introduction to the chapter should you wish to explore the area further. The numbered boxes in *green* represent each pub or inn in the area selected. For more information on the pub or inn simply locate the same number within the chapter (to the left of the pub/inn name) to find the name, address, telephone number and facilities of the pub or inn.

Finding a Specific Pub or Inn

If you know the name of the pub or inn and its location then simply go to the relevant chapter where the names of the pubs are listed in alphabetical order.

Pub and Inn Information

All pubs or inns in the guide give details of the name, address, telephone number and whether they offer real ales, food, accommodation and no smoking areas.

The advertising panels found in each chapter provide more comprehensive information on the pub or inn such as contact details, location, interior and exterior facilities, real ales, opening times, food, entertainment, disabled access, credit cards and places of interest.

Location Map

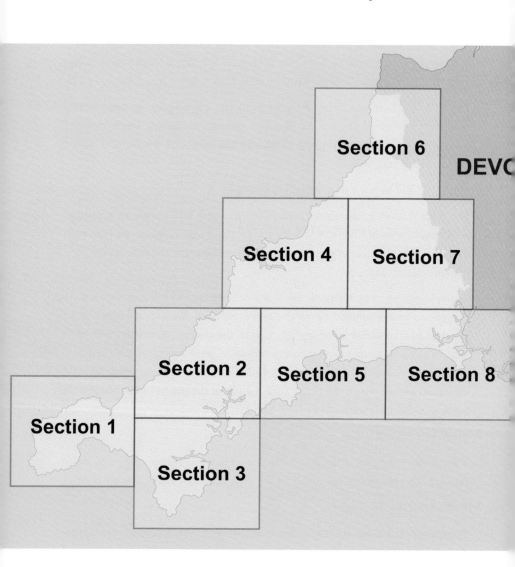

Contents

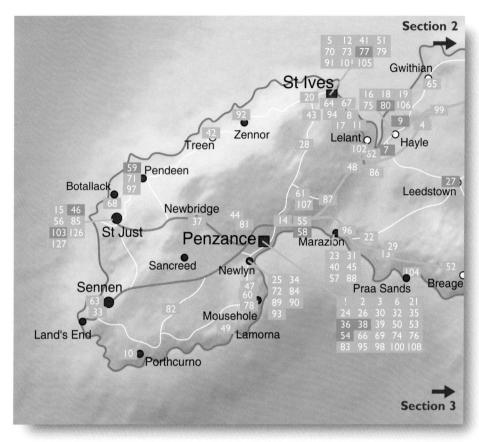

Section 2

5 12 41 51
70 73 77 79
91 101 105

Gwithian
65

St Ives

20
64 67   16 18 19
43 94 8   75 80 106
17 11
9   4

92

Zennor

Treen
42

Lelant
102 62 7   Hayle

28

Pendeen
59
71
97

48
86

Botallack
68

27
Leedstown

15 46
56 85
103 126
127

Newbridge
37   44   81

14 55
58 96 22
61 107 87
29
13

St Just

Penzance

Marazion

Sancreed

Newlyn

23 31
40 45
57 88

104
52

Breage

Sennen
63
33

82

25 34
72 84
89 90
47
60
78
93

Praa Sands

Mousehole
49

Lamorna

1 2 3 6 21
24 26 30 32 35
36 38 39 50 53
54 66 69 74 76
83 95 98 100 108

Land's End

10

Porthcurno

Section 3

11   Pub or Inn Reference Number - Detailed Information

12   Pub or Inn Reference Number - Summary Entry

● ■   Place of interest mentioned in the chapter introduction

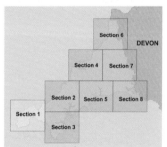

Section 6

DEVON

Section 4   Section 7

Section 2   Section 5   Section 8

Section 1

Section 3

WEST CORNWALL

One of the most famous places in Britain, Lands End lies at the country's western tip, where the granite land meets the wild Atlantic. All of Cornwall's major attractions are represented in this part of the county: the legacy of the sea at Newlyn and Penzance, the mining industry at Geevor, bird-lovers venues at Marazion and Mousehole and the artistic tradition at Newlyn and St Ives, where the Tate Gallery and the Barbara Hepworth Sculpture Garden and Museum are among the most important in the country.

Botallack

Overlooking the coast are the remains of the old engine houses of **Boatallack Mine**, the underground workings of which once went out beneath the sea bed.

Land's End

One of the country's most famous landmarks, a spectacular place where the granite on which most of Cornwall stands meets the Atlantic Ocean in an awesome series of cliffs, reefs and sheer-sided inlets.

Marazion

One of Cornwall's oldest chartered towns, with a number of fine old buildings overlooking the sandy beach. The town **Museum** is housed in the Town Hall. To the north is **Marazion Marsh & RSPB Reserve**, an extensive area of wetland and reed beds.

Mousehole

The epitome of a Cornish fishing village, Mousehole was described as the 'loveliest village in England' by Dylan Thomas, who honeymooned here in 1937. On the cliffs at Raginnis Hill is the **Mousehole Wild Bird Hospital and Sanctuary**, which was at its busiest at the time of the *Torrey Canyon* disaster, when over 8,000 oil-affected birds were treated. Mousehole's parish church is in the neighbouring village of **Paul**, where a memorial in the churchyard wall marks the grave of Dolly Pentreath, the last person in Cornwall to speak only the native tongue Kerneweck.

Newlyn

The largest fish-landing port in England and Wales, and the home base for about 200 vessels. Pilchards are still an important catch,

Mousehole

and the process of salting and preserving them can be seen by visitors to the **Pilchard Works Museum & Factory**. The exceptionally clear natural light enjoyed by Newlyn has always attracted artists, and the **Newlyn School of Artists** developed from the 1880s onwards. **Newlyn Art Gallery** is a showcase for artists living and working in Newlyn today.

Pendeen

The last of the 20 or so mines in the area to close (in 1990) was the Geevor Tin Mine, now extensively preserved as the **Geevor Tin Mine and Heritage Centre**. Nearby is the **Levant Beam Engine**, the oldest working steam engine in the country. These sights can both be toured, as can Pendeen Lighthouse on the slate promontory of Pendeen Watch.

Penzance

A bustling town and harbour, with a promenade that stretches all the way to Newlyn. Most of the town's many interesting buildings stand on Chapel Street, including the domed **Market House**, the exotic **Egyptian House** and the **Union Hotel**, from where the first mainland announcement was made of the victory at Waterloo and the death of Nelson. Displays of local history and the work of the Newlyn School of Artists can be seen at the **Penlee House Art Gallery & Museum**. By the harbour, the **Trinity House Lighthouse Centre** tells the interesting story of lighthouses and lighthouse keeping.

Porthcurno

It was from here, in 1870, that the first telegraph cable was laid, and the **Porthcurno Telegraph Museum** explains the technology that has been developed from Victorian times to the present day. The major part of the museum is housed in bomb-proof wartime tunnels. Porthcurno is also home to the unqiue **Minack Theatre**, an open-air amphitheatre cut into the high cliffs.

Praa Sands

Two headlands and high dunes enclose the mile-long crescent of sand that have helped to make Praa Sands one of the finest family beaches in the county.

Sancreed

In the churchyard of the 15th century **Church of St**

Penzance

Credan are five Celtic crosses, and in the surrounding area are two ancinet monuments, the **Blind Fiddler** and the **Two Sisters**, both said to represent human beings turned to stone for committing irreligious acts on the Sabbath.

St Ives

With its sandy beaches, picturesque harbour and headland, its maze of narrow streets and its artistic heritage, this beautifully situated fishing town is deservedly one of the most visited places in the Southwest. It has two of the most important centres of the arts in the whole country, the **Tate Gallery** and the **Barbara Hepworth Sculpture Garden and Museum**.

St Just

The westernmost town in Great Britain, with a 15th century parish church, a thriving arts scene and an grassy amphitheatre where an annual carnival takes place and 500-year-old miracle plays are performed in Cornish.

St Michael's Mount

A third of a mile offshore and connected to Marazion by a cobbled causeway, St Michael's Mount is a remarkable slate and granite outcrop that has been inhabited since prehistoric times. **St Michael's Mount Castle**, in the care of the National Trust since 1964, is a fine battlemented building with many interesting architectural features and artefacts.

Sennen

The most westerly village in England, with superb cliff walks along the coast to Land's End. The sandy beach at Sennen Cove is ideal for both bathing and surfing.

Zennor

The **Wayside Folk Museum** has numerous exhibits that tell of the region's industrial past. In the garden are two waterwheels from the mining industry and a collection of ancient corn-grinding querns and stone tools. On the granite moorland southeast of the village lies **Zennor Quoit**, one of several Neolithic chamber tombs in the region.

St Michaels Mount

1 The Abbey Hotel and Restaurant

Abbey Street, Penzance, Cornwall TR18 4AR
Tel: 01736 366906

Real Ales, Bar Food, Restaurant Menu,
Accommodation, No Smoking Area, Disabled Facilities

2 Admiral Benbow

46 Chapel Street, Penzance, Cornwall TR18 4AL
Tel: 01736 363448

Real Ales, Bar Food, Restaurant Menu,
No Smoking Area

3 Alexandra Inn

Alexandra Rd, Penzance, Cornwall TR18 4LY
Tel: 01736 365165

Real Ales, Bar Food, Accommodation

4 Angarrack Inn

12 Steamers Hill, Angarrack, Hayle,
Cornwall TR27 5JB
Tel: 01736 752380

Real Ales, Restaurant Menu, No Smoking Area

5 Balnoon Inn

The Old Coach Road, St Ives, Cornwall TR26 3JB
Tel: 01736 797572

Real Ales, Restaurant Menu, Accommodation,
No Smoking Area, Disabled Facilities

6 The Bath Inn

Cornwall Terrace, Penzance, Cornwall TR18 4HL
Tel: 01736 331940

Real Ales, Bar Food, No Smoking Area

7 The Bird in Hand

Trelissick Road, Hayle, Cornwall TR27 4HY
☎ 01736 753974

Real Ales, Bar Food, Restaurant Menu,
No Smoking Area, Disabled Facilities

☛ A30 to Hayle, then through town to Paradise Park

🍺 Three Wheal Ales brewed on site

🍴 Snacks and full menu

🎵 Live music Saturday(sometimes Friday)

⛏ Car park, garden

💳 Major cards

🕐 11-11

🏛 Paradise Park adjacent; Hayle beaches and estuary 1 mile, RSPB Reserve 1 mile, St Ives 3 miles

Right next to the popular family attraction Paradise Park, **The Bird in Hand** is a handsome stone building that was originally the coaching house to the Park before being converted to an inn in the 1970s. Both inside and out there are reminders of the inn's past and of Hayle, including feeding hoppers and an imposing painting showing the town's industrial heritage. The Wheal Ale Brewery on site produces three excellent real ales, and customers will also find a good selection of other beers, stouts and lagers, ciders, wines, spirits and soft drinks. Home-cooked food is another attraction, ranging from light snacks to full meals, and the printed menu is supplemented by daily specials. In fine weather barbecues are held in the beer garden, which sports the largest parasol in Hayle. Major sports events are shown on a vast TV screen at one end of the bar, and live music sessions take place on Saturdays.

7 Bird In Hand

Trelissick Road, Hayle, Cornwall TR27 4HY
Tel: 01736 753974

Real Ales, Bar Food, Restaurant Menu,
No Smoking Area, Disabled Facilities

See panel opposite

8 Boskerris Hotel

Boskerris Road, Carbis Bay, St Ives,
Cornwall TR26 2NK
Tel: 01736 795295

Real Ales, Bar Food, Restaurant Menu,
Accommodation, No Smoking Area, Disabled Facilities

9 The Bucket of Blood

13 Church Town Rd, Phillack, Hayle,
Cornwall TR27 5AE
Tel: 01736 752378

Real Ales, Bar Food

See panel below

9 The Bucket of Blood

Phillack, nr Hayle, Cornwall TR27 5AE
☎ 01736 752378

Real Ales, Bar Food

- In Phillack, a short distance east of Hayle
- HSD, Dartmoor
- Winter: Lunch Thurs-Sun, Dinner 7 days; summer Wed-Sat Dinner only
- Garden, patio, car park
- Major cards except Amex and Diners
- Lunchtime and evening
- Hayle 1 mile

In the picturesque village of Phillack, just outside Hayle, the **Bucket of Blood** has long been a favourite with local residents and the many visitors to the region.

In the Shackleton family for over 40 years, the inn is full of warmth and character, an ideal spot for enjoying a drink in the bar or pretty garden or a meal featuring prime local produce.

10 Cable Station

Porthcurno, St Levan, Penzance, Cornwall TR19 6JX
Tel: 01736 810479

Real Ales, Bar Food, Restaurant Menu,
Accommodation, No Smoking Area, Disabled Facilities

11 Carbis Bay Hotel

Carbis Bay, St Ives, Cornwall TR26 2NP
Tel: 01736 795311

Bar Food, Restaurant Menu, Accommodation,
No Smoking Area, Disabled Facilities

12 Castle Inn

Fore Street, St Ives, Cornwall TR26 1AB
Tel: 01736 796833

Real Ales, Bar Food

13 Coach and Horses Inn

Kenneggy Downs, Rosudgeon, Penzance,
Cornwall TR20 9AW
Tel: 01736 762470

Real Ales, Bar Food, No Smoking Area

14 Coldstreamer Inn

Gulval, Penzance, Cornwall TR18 3BB
Tel: 01736 362072

Real Ales, Bar Food, Restaurant Menu,
No Smoking Area, Disabled Facilities

15 Commercial Hotel

Market Square, StJust, Penzance,
Cornwall TR19 7HE
Tel: 01736 788455

Real Ales, Bar Food, Restaurant Menu,
Accommodation, No Smoking Area, Disabled Facilities

16 Copperhouse Inn

11 Fore St, Hayle, Cornwall TR27 4DX
Tel: 01736 756768

Real Ales, No Smoking Area, Disabled Facilities

17 The Cornish Arms

Carbis Bay, St Ives, Cornwall TR26 2PG
Tel: 01736 796112

Real Ales, Bar Food, No Smoking Area

18 Cornish Arms
86 Commercial Rd, Hayle, Cornwall TR27 4DJ
Tel: 01736 753237

Real Ales, Bar Food, Restaurant Menu,
No Smoking Area, Disabled Facilities

19 Cornubia Inn
Copperhouse, Hayle, Cornwall TR27 4DX
Tel: 01736 753351

Real Ales, Bar Food, Restaurant Menu,
Accommodation, No Smoking Area, Disabled Facilities

20 The Croft
Penbeagle Lane, St Ives, Cornwall TR26 2EY
Tel: 01736 797473

Real Ales, No Smoking Area

21 Crown Inn
Victoria Square, Penzance, Cornwall TR18 2EP
Tel: 01736 351070

Real Ales, Bar Food, Restaurant Menu,
No Smoking Area, Disabled Facilities

22 The Crown Inn
Fore Street, Goldsinthney, Penzance,
Cornwall TR20 9LG
Tel: 01736 710494

Real Ales, Bar Food, Restaurant Menu,
No Smoking Area

23 Cutty Sark/ Marazion Hotel
The Square, Marazion, Cornwall TR17 0AP
Tel: 01736 710334

Real Ales, Bar Food, Restaurant Menu,
Accommodation, No Smoking Area, Disabled Facilities

24 The Dock Inn
17 Quay St, Penzance, Cornwall TR18 4BD
Tel: 01736 362833

Real Ales, Accommodation, No Smoking Area

25 The Dolphin Inn Ltd
Jack Lane, Newlyn, Penzance, Cornwall TR18 5HZ
Tel: 01736 366253

Disabled Facilities

26 The Dolphin Tavern
Quay Street, Penzance, Cornwall TR18 4BD
Tel: 01736 364106

Real Ales, Bar Food, Restaurant Menu,
No Smoking Area

27 Duke Of Leeds
Hayle Road, Leedstown, Hayle, Cornwall TR27 6DB
Tel: 01736 850273

Bar Food, Restaurant Menu, Accommodation,
No Smoking Area

See panel below

27 Duke of Leeds Inn
Hayle Road, Leedstown, Hayle,
Cornwall TR27 6DB
☎ 01736 850273

**Bar Food, Restaurant Menu, Accommodation,
No Smoking Area**

☛ At the junction of the B3280 and B3302 4 miles S of Hayle

🍴 12-2 & 6-9; all day in summer

🛏 5 rooms

🍺 Beer garden, car park

💳 Major cards except Amex and Diners

🕐 All day in summer

🏛 Hayle 4 miles, Helston 6 miles, Penzance 10 miles

Owner Salvatore Correnti is the friendly host at the **Duke of Leeds Inn**, which stands on a prominent corner site in a village between Hayle and Helston. The chef makes excellent use of local produce on his menus, which include a popular Sunday lunch centred round a choice of roasts with all the traditional trimmings. Five upstairs rooms provide year-round accommodation for B&B guests, and the pub has a pleasant beer garden.

28 The Engine Inn

Cripples Ease, Penzance, Cornwall TR20 8NF
Tel: 01736 740204

Real Ales, Bar Food, Restaurant Menu,
Accommodation

29 Falmouth Packet Inn

Rosudgeon, Penzance, Cornwall TR20 9QE
Tel: 01736 762240

Real Ales, Bar Food, Restaurant Menu,
Disabled Facilities

30 Farmers Arms

Causewayhead Road, Penzance,
Cornwall TR18 2ST
Tel: 01736 362627

Real Ales

31 Fire Engine Inn

Higher Fore Street, Marazion, Cornwall TR17 0BB
Tel: 01736 710562

Real Ales, Bar Food, No Smoking Area

32 First and Last Inn

Ambulance Station ,Alverton Road, Penzance,
Cornwall TR18 4TN
Tel: 01736 364095

Real Ales, Bar Food, No Smoking Area,
Disabled Facilities

33 First and Last Inn

Sennen, Penzance, Cornwall TR19 7AD
Tel: 01736 871680

Real Ales, Bar Food, Restaurant Menu,
No Smoking Area, Disabled Facilities

34 Fishermans Arms Inn

Fore Street, Newlyn, Penzance, Cornwall TR18 5JR
Tel: 01736 363399

Real Ales, Bar Food, Disabled Facilities

35 Flanagans Bar

3 East Terrace, Penzance, Cornwall TR18 2TD
Tel: 01736 363181

Real Ales

36 Flicks

52 Market Jew St, Penzance, Cornwall TR18 2HZ
Tel: 01736 364494

Bar Food, Disabled Facilities

See panel below

36 Flick's

52 Market Jew Street, Penzance,
Cornwall TR18 2HZ
☎ 01736 364494

Bar Food, Disabled Facilities

☞ In the town centre close to many attractions

🍴 11-10.45

💳 Cash only

🕐 11-11 (Closed Sunday)

🏛 The attractions of Penzance; Newlyn 1 mile, Mousehole 2½ miles, Lamorna Cove 4 miles

Here on one of the main streets of Penzance, manager Tamsyn and assistant manager Tara provide excellent hospitality for young and old, locals and visitors.

Flick's has a stylish, contemporary look, crating a relaxed, cheerful ambience for enjoying a drink and lively conversation. Buster Breakfast is served from 11 to 2, with pizzas and basket meals available throughout opening hours.

37 Fountain Inn

Newbridge, Nr Penzance, Cornwall TR20 8QH
Tel: 01736 364075

Real Ales, Bar Food, Restaurant Menu,
No Smoking Area, Disabled Facilities

38 Fountain Tavern

St Clare Street, Penzance, Cornwall TR18 2PD
Tel: 01736 362673

Real Ales, Bar Food, Accommodation

See panel on page 10

38 The Fountain Tavern

St Clare Street, Penzance, Cornwall TR18 2PD
☎ 01736 362673
⊕ www.fountaintavern.co.uk

Real Ales, Bar Food, Accommodation

- ☛ A short walk from the centre of Penzance
- 🍺 HSD, Tinners
- ⊢⊣ 3 en suite rooms
- 🏭 Public car park adjacent
- ✖ Cash only
- 🕐 Lunchtime and evening
- 🏛 All the attractions of Penzance; Land's End 10 miles

The Fountain Tavern is a popular place to unwind and enjoy the hospitality provided by tenants Allan and Ruth. Nautical and aviation pictures hang in the well-furnished bar. The Fountain caters for overnight guests with three good-quality rooms for B&B.

39 Globe and Ale House

Queen Street, Penzance, Cornwall TR18 4BJ
Tel: 01736 364098

Real Ales

40 Godolphin Arms

West End, Marazion, Cornwall TR17 0EN
Tel: 01736 710202

Bar Food, Restaurant Menu, Accommodation, No Smoking Area, Disabled Facilities

41 Golden Lion

Market Place, St Ives, Cornwall TR26 1RZ
Tel: 01736 793679

Real Ales, Bar Food, Disabled Facilities

42 Gurnards Head Hotel

Treen, Zennor, St Ives, Cornwall TR26 3DE
Tel: 01736 796928

Real Ales, Bar Food, Restaurant Menu, Accommodation, No Smoking Area

43 The Halsetown Inn

Halsetown, St Ives, Cornwall TR26 3NA
Tel: 01736 795583

Real Ales, Bar Food, Restaurant Menu, Accommodation, No Smoking Area

44 King William The Fourth

Church Road, Madron, Penzance, Cornwall TR20 8SS
Tel: 01736 363022

Real Ales, Bar Food, Restaurant Menu, No Smoking Area, Disabled Facilities

45 Kings Arms

The Square, Marazion, Cornwall TR17 0AP
Tel: 01736 710291

Real Ales, Bar Food, Disabled Facilities

46 Kings Arms

Market Square, St Just, Penzance, Cornwall TR19 7HF
Tel: 01736 788545

Real Ales, Bar Food, Accommodation, Disabled Facilities

See panel opposite

47 Kings Arms Inn

Paul, Penzance, Cornwall TR19 6TZ
Tel: 01736 731224

Real Ales, Bar Food, Restaurant Menu, No Smoking Area, Disabled Facilities

48 Lamb and Flag

Canonstown, Hayle, Cornwall TR27 6LU
Tel: 01736 753289

Real Ales, Bar Food, Restaurant Menu, No Smoking Area, Disabled Facilities

46 The Kings Arms

5 Market Square, St Just, Cornwall TR19 7HF
☎ 01736 788545

Real Ales, Bar Food, Accommodation,
Disabled Facilities

- In the market square of St Just, 6 miles NW of Penzance on the A3071
- St Austell Tinners and Tribute
- 12-2 (2.30 in summer) & 6-9 (9.30 in summer)
- 2 bedrooms
- Quiz Wednesday, live music I Saturday a month
- Seats at front
- Major cards except Amex and Diners
- 11-11 (Sun 12-10.30)
- Penzance 6 miles

By the 15th century church in mainland Britain's westernmost town, the Kings Arms is rich in history and tradition. Behind the sturdy stone frontage, decked in spring and summer with window boxes and hanging baskets, the bar and dining areas feature thick stone walls, beams and country-style chairs set at polished darkwood tables. The pub is very much a family affair, run since 1999 by Alan and Janet McCall and helped by son Damian and Netta – both cooks – and Krystle behind the bar. The printed menu and daily specials tempt with a wide range of meat, fish and vegetarian dishes based on locally sourced ingredients – fresh trout is a very popular choice. The Kings Arms has two upstairs bedrooms for B&B guests.

49 Lamorna Wink

Lamorna, Penzance, Cornwall TR19 6XH
Tel: 01736 731566

Real Ales, Bar Food, No Smoking Area

50 Lamp and Whistle Inn

Leskinnick Place, Penzance, Cornwall TR18 2EZ
Tel: 01736 363420

51 Lifeboat Inn

Wharf Road, St Ives, Cornwall TR26 ILF
Tel: 01736 794123

Real Ales, Bar Food, Restaurant Menu,
Accommodation, No Smoking Area, Disabled Facilities

52 Lion and Lamb

Fore Street, Ashton, Helston, Cornwall TR13 9RW
Tel: 01736 763227

Real Ales, Bar Food, Restaurant Menu,
No Smoking Area, Disabled Facilities

53 Longboat Hotel

Market Jew St, Penzance, Cornwall TR18 2HZ
Tel: 01736 364137

Real Ales, Bar Food, Restaurant Menu,
Accommodation, No Smoking Area

54 Lugger Hotel and Wheelhouse Restaurant

The Promenade, Penzance, Cornwall TR18 4DL
Tel: 01736 363236

Real Ales, Bar Food, Restaurant Menu,
Accommodation, No Smoking Area, Disabled Facilities

See panel on page 12

55 Mexico Inn

Gladstone Terrace, Long Rock, Cornwall TR20 8JB
Tel: 01736 710625

Real Ales, Bar Food, Restaurant Menu,
No Smoking Area, Disabled Facilities

54 The Lugger Hotel & Wheelhouse Restaurant

The Promenade, Penzance, Cornwall TR18 4DL
☎ 01736 363236
🌐 www.theluggerhotel.co.uk

Real Ales, Bar Food, Restaurant Menu, Accommodation, No Smoking Area, Disabled Facilities

- 🖝 On the seafront in Penzance
- 🍷 Selection
- 🍴 Summer 12-5 & 6-10, Winter 6-10 (weekends 12-9.30)
- 🛏 24 rooms en suite
- 🍹 Terrace overlooking seafront
- 💳 Major cards except Amex and Diners
- 🕐 Summer all day, Winter evenings + all day weekends
- 🏛 Newlyn 2 miles, St Michael's Mount 3 miles, Land's End 10 miles

In a marvellous setting on the only promenade in Cornwall, the **Lugger Hotel & Wheelhouse Restaurant** is an ideal holiday base and a place to seek out for a great meal. The hotel has been developed from three cottages into a classic seaside hotel with 24 well-appointed rooms of various sizes, most of them with en suite facilities and the majority enjoying superb views. Lovely flower displays adorn the outside of the building, and the front terrace overlooking the sea is the number one spot to be when the sun shines. Owner Lesley Ashcroft, partner Shane Triggs and their staff ensure that any visit here, whether for a drink (a selection of real ales is always available), a meal or a longer stay, will be an occasion to remember.

The present owners created the lovely Wheelhouse Restaurant, which commands views of Mounts Bay, St Michael's Mount and the Lizard Peninsula. Various menus provide an excellent choice of food, from bar snacks and light lunches to a full à la carte selection. A popular carvery, with four meats and a vegetarian option, operates daily in summer and on Friday, Saturday and Sunday out of season. The best and freshest English ingredients, including fish from Newlyn, is the

basis of the dishes, and Lesley and her kitchen team have established a reputation that is second to none in the region.

Typical seafood specials – the choice changes constantly – might include crab thermidor, deep-fried squid with chilli mayonnaise, sea bass baked with basil and mushrooms, and sea bream with herbs, tomatoes and olives. Meat dishes such as loin of pork with mushrooms and a wholegrain mustard sauce are equally delicious, and there's always a choice for vegetarians, with scrumptious desserts to finish. The atmosphere throughout the hotel is delightfully informal and relaxed, and it's no surprise that it's a very popular venue for special celebrations as well as meetings and conferences.

56 The Miners Arms
9 Bank St, StJust, Penzance, Cornwall TR19 7HJ
Tel: 01736 788484

Real Ales

---

57 Mount Haven Hotel
Turnpike Road, Marazion, Cornwall TR17 0DQ
Tel: 01736 710249

Real Ales, Bar Food, Restaurant Menu,
Accommodation, No Smoking Area

---

58 Mount View Hotel
Long Rock, Penzance, Cornwall TR20 8JJ
Tel: 01736 710416

Real Ales, Bar Food, Accommodation,
No Smoking Area, Disabled Facilities

See panel below

---

59 North Inn
The Square, Pendeen, Penzance,
Cornwall TR19 7DN
Tel: 01736 788417

Real Ales, Bar Food, Restaurant Menu,
Accommodation, No Smoking Area, Disabled Facilities

See panel on page 14

---

60 Old Coastguard Hotel
The Parade, Mousehole, Penzance,
Cornwall TR19 6PR
Tel: 01736 731222

Real Ales, Bar Food, Restaurant Menu,
Accommodation, No Smoking Area, Disabled Facilities

---

58 Mount View Hotel
Long Rock, Penzance, Cornwall TR20 8JJ
☎ 01736 710416

🌐 www.cornishtouristboard/penzance.co.uk

**Real Ales, Bar Food, Accommodation,
No Smoking Area, Disabled Facilities**

- ☛ Long Rock stands off the A30 between Penzance and Marazion
- 🍺 Adnam's Broadside + guests
- 🍴 Home-cooked snacks and meals lunchtime and evening
- 🛏 5 rooms (3 en suite)
- 🎵 Pool, darts, monthly quiz
- 🅿 Car park
- 💳 Major cards
- 🕐 11-11 (Sun 12-4 & 7-10.30)
- 🏛 Penzance 2 miles, Marazion 2 miles, St Michael's Mount 1 mile

With five well-appointed guest bedrooms, three of them fully en suite, the **Mount View Hotel** sits off the A30 close to the shore between Penzance and Marazion. Built from local stone in 1894 and comfortably updated, this small family-run hotel prides itself on providing great value for money, and the friendly, welcoming atmosphere makes it an excellent choice for a relaxing holiday in a picturesque part of Cornwall.

The bedrooms all have television, tea/coffee making facilities and toiletries. The hotel is also a popular 'local', with a cosy bar and a separate non-smoking restaurant where an extensive, frequently changing menu includes popular dishes such as home-made pies, steaks and spaghetti bolognese as well as Cornish fish specials and vegetarian choices. Toasted sandwiches and jacket potatoes fit the bill for lighter meals, accompanied perhaps by a glass of Adnam's Broadside.

59 North Inn

The Square, Pendeen, nr Penzance,
Cornwall TR19 7DN
☎ 01736 788417

🌐 www.thenorthinnpendeen.co.uk

Real Ales, Bar Food, Restaurant Menu, Accommodation, No Smoking Area, Disabled Facilities

- The pub is in the centre of Pendeen, 6 miles NW of Penzance on the B3306
- St Austell ales
- Full selection of snacks and meals
- 4 chalet-style rooms
- Darts
- Garden with sea views; camping field adjacent
- Major cards
- CAMRA and Community Pub awards
- 11-11
- Geevor Tin Mines ½ mile, Levant Steam Engine 1 mile, St Just 2 miles, Penzance 6 miles

Dating back to the early 18th century, the North Inn is a splendid creeper-clad pub in the centre of the attractive village of Pendeen, six miles west of Penzance. Landlord John Coak, here for 7 years, has made this one of the best run and most popular pubs in the region, fully deserving its many accolades, including CAMRA Cornwall Pub of the Year and Community Pub of the Year.

A choice of 4 real ales are served all day in the traditionally styled bar, along with a good selection of other beers, lagers, wines and spirits, and local meat and fish features prominently among the great food that keeps the customers happy every lunchtime and evening. The North Inn is also a perfect base for tourists, and the four chalet-style bedrooms in the garden provide every comfort. The inn also has a village shop (open all day) and a camping site in the adjacent field.

61 Old Inn

Lower Quarter, Ludgvan, Penzance,
Cornwall TR20 8EG
Tel: 01736 740419

Real Ales, Bar Food, Restaurant Menu,
Accommodation, No Smoking Area, Disabled Facilities

62 Old Quay House Inn

Griggs Quay, Hayle, Cornwall TR27 6JG
Tel: 01736 753988

Real Ales, Bar Food, Restaurant Menu,
Accommodation, No Smoking Area, Disabled Facilities

63 Old Success Inn

Sennen Cove, Penzance, Cornwall TR19 7DG
Tel: 01736 871232

Real Ales, Bar Food, Restaurant Menu,
Accommodation, No Smoking Area, Disabled Facilities

64 Pedn-Olva Hotel

Porthminster Beach, St Ives, Cornwall TR26 2EA
Tel: 01736 796222

Real Ales, Bar Food, Restaurant Menu,
Accommodation, No Smoking Area, Disabled Facilities

65 Pendarves Arms

Prosper Hill, Gwithian, Hayle, Cornwall TR27 5BW
Tel: 01736 753223

Real Ales, Bar Food, Restaurant Menu

66 Peruvian Arms

Mount Street, Penzance, Cornwall TR18 2EU
Tel: 01736 331411

Real Ales

67 Portminster Hotel

The Terrace, St Ives, Cornwall TR26 2BN
Tel: 01736 795221

Bar Food, Restaurant Menu, Accommodation,
No Smoking Area, Disabled Facilities

68 Queens Arms

Botallack, St Just, Penzance, Cornwall TR19 7QG
Tel: 01736 788318

Real Ales, Bar Food, Restaurant Menu,
Accommodation, No Smoking Area, Disabled Facilities

69 Queens Hotel

The Promenade, Penzance, Cornwall TR18 4HG
Tel: 01736 362371

Real Ales, Bar Food, Restaurant Menu,
Accommodation, No Smoking Area, Disabled Facilities

70 Queen's Tavern

High Street, St Ives, Cornwall TR26 1RR
Tel: 01736 796468

Real Ales, Bar Food, Accommodation

71 Radjel Inn

Boscaswell Terrace, Pendeen, Penzance,
Cornwall TR19 7DS
Tel: 01736 788446

Real Ales, Bar Food, Accommodation,
No Smoking Area, Disabled Facilities

72 Red Lion Inn

36 Fore Street, Newlyn, Penzance,
Cornwall TR18 5JP
Tel: 01736 362012

Real Ales, Bar Food

73 The Reef Bar

The Wharf, St Ives, Cornwall TR26 1LP
Tel: 01736 798482

Restaurant Menu, No Smoking Area

74 The Regent Bar

Chapel St, Penzance, Cornwall TR18 4AE
Tel: 01736 362946

Real Ales, Restaurant Menu, No Smoking Area

75 Royal Standard Inn

61 Penpol Terrace, Hayle, Cornwall TR27 4BH
Tel: 01736 753350

Real Ales

77 The Sheaf of Wheat

Chapel Street, St Ives, Cornwall TR26 2LS
☎ 01736 797130 ⊕ www.sheafofwheat.co.uk

**Real Ales, Bar Food, Restaurant Menu,
No Smoking Area, Disabled Facilities**

☛ In the heart of St Ives
🍺 St Austell Tribute
🍴 11-9
⛱ Patio
💳 Major cards except Amex and Diners
🕐 11-11 (Sun 12-10.30)
🏛 All the attractions of St Ives

With a brilliant floral display to rival anything in the county, the **Sheaf of Wheat** is one of the most popular and convivial of all the pubs in the region.

Run for 12 years by tenants Eric and Linda Bloxam, the pub has both public and lounge bars offering a choice for drinkers, with a beer garden providing an alfresco option in warm weather. Three to four real ales and an excellent selection of beers, lagers, ciders and wines can be enjoyed on their own or to accompany a variety of meals to suit all tastes.

In addition to the wide-ranging main menu there's a very well patronised carvery (best to book) at the weekend and children are welcome. The pub has two sports TV screens as well as pool

76 The Seven Stars
Parade Street, Penzance, Cornwall TR18 4BU
Tel: 01736 362733

Real Ales

77 Sheaf of Wheat Inn
Connaught Cottage, Chapel Street, St Ives,
Cornwall TR26 2LS
Tel: 01736 797130

Real Ales, Bar Food, Restaurant Menu,
No Smoking Area, Disabled Facilities

See panel on page 15

78 Ship Inn
South Cliff, Mousehole, Penzance,
Cornwall TR19 6QX
Tel: 01736 731234

Real Ales, Bar Food, Restaurant Menu,
Accommodation, No Smoking Area

79 The Sloop Inn
The Wharf, St Ives, Cornwall TR26 1LP
Tel: 01736 796584

Real Ales, Bar Food, Accommodation,
No Smoking Area

80 Smugglers
St Erth Praze, Hayle, Cornwall TR27 6EG
Tel: 01736 850280

Real Ales, Bar Food, Restaurant Menu,
Accommodation, No Smoking Area

See panel below

81 Sportsmans Arms
Bolitho Road, Heamoor, Penzance,
Cornwall TR18 3EH
Tel: 01736 362831

Real Ales

80 The Smugglers
St Erth Praze, Hayle, Cornwall TR27 6EG
☎ 01736 850280
🌐 www.smugglersstives.co.uk

**Real Ales, Bar Food, Restaurant Menu,
Accommodation, No Smoking Area**

- On the B3302 2 miles S of Hayle
- Skinners, St Austell, Directors
- 12-9.30
- 3 en suite rooms + 2 flats
- Jazz Sun L, Cornish Folk Music Sun eve, salsa dancing Tues
- Beer garden, car park
- Major cards accepted
- 11-11 (Sun 12-10.30)
- Hayle 2 miles, St Ives 6 miles, Trevarno 7 miles, Helston 8 miles

Open all day, every day for both food and drink, the **Smugglers Inn** has a warm welcome for the whole family. Malcolm and Nikkie Hall have made many friends since taking over in 2002, and the pub attracts a steady band of regulars and visitors with its outstanding food, which is served from noon to 9.30 daily. The menu tempts with an exceptionally wide choice of meat, fish and vegetarian dishes, and booking is recommended, especially for the traditional Sunday roasts. The Smugglers is a good choice for overnight stays or longer breaks, and guests can choose between three en suite double rooms and two well-appointed flats. The inn is also one of the most sociable in the region, with live music on Sunday, Tuesday and Wednesday. The Jazz Club was established 35 years ago, and the pub is also home to the St Ives Folk Club (meets Sunday evening)

82 St Buryan Inn

St Buryan, Penzance, Cornwall TR19 6BA
Tel: 01736 810385

Real Ales, Bar Food, Restaurant Menu

83 The Star Inn

Market Jew Street, Penzance, Cornwall TR18 2LD
Tel: 01736 363241

Bar Food, Restaurant Menu, Disabled Facilities

84 The Star Inn

The Strand , Newlyn, Penzance,
Cornwall TR18 5HW
Tel: 01736 368674

Real Ales

85 Star Inn

1 Fore Street, StJust, Penzance, Cornwall TR19 7LL
Tel: 01736 788767

Real Ales, No Smoking Area, Disabled Facilities

86 The Star Inn

1 Church Street, St Erth, Hayle,
Cornwall TR27 6HP
Tel: 01736 752068

Real Ales, Bar Food, Restaurant Menu,
Accommodation

87 Star Inn

Crowlas, Penzance, Cornwall TR20 8DX
Tel: 01736 740375

Real Ales, Bar Food, Restaurant Menu,
Accommodation, No Smoking Area

88 Station Freehouse and Restaurant

Seafront, Marazion, Penzance, Cornwall TR17 0DA
Tel: 01736 350459

Real Ales, Bar Food, Restaurant Menu,
No Smoking Area, Disabled Facilities

89 Swordfish Inn

The Strand, Newlyn, Penzance,
Cornwall TR18 5HN
Tel: 01736 362830

Real Ales, Bar Food, Restaurant Menu,
No Smoking Area, Disabled Facilities

90 Tarbet Hotel

11-12 Clarence Street, Newlyn, Penzance,
Cornwall TR18 2NU
Tel: 01736 363758

Real Ales, Bar Food, Restaurant Menu,
Accommodation, No Smoking Area

91 Three Ferrets

17 Chapel Street, St Ives, Cornwall TR26 2LR
Tel: 01736 795364

Real Ales

92 Tinners Arms

Zennor, Cornwall TR26 3BY
Tel: 01736 796927

Real Ales, Bar Food, Restaurant Menu,
Accommodation, No Smoking Area, Disabled Facilities

93 Tolcarne Inn

Tolcarne Place, Newlyn, Nr Penzance,
Cornwall TR18 5AH
Tel: 01736 363074

Real Ales, Bar Food, Restaurant Menu, No Smoking
Area, Disabled Facilities

94 Tregenna Castle

Treloyhan Avenue, St Ives, Cornwall TR26 2DE
Tel: 01736 795254

Real Ales, Restaurant Menu, Accommodation,
No Smoking Area, Disabled Facilities

95 The Tremenheere

4-6 Market Place, Penzance, Cornwall TR18 2JA
Tel: 01736 335350

Real Ales, Bar Food, Restaurant Menu,
No Smoking Area, Disabled Facilities

96 The Trevelyan Arms
Fore Street, Goldsinthney, Penzance,
Cornwall TR20 9JU
Tel: 01736 710453

Real Ales, Bar Food, Restaurant Menu,
Accommodation, No Smoking Area, Disabled Facilities

97 Trewallard Arms Hotel
Trewallard Road, Pendeen, Nr St Just,
Cornwall TR19 7PW
Tel: 01736 788634

Real Ales, Bar Food, Restaurant Menu,
Accommodation, No Smoking Area, Disabled Facilities

98 Turks Head Inn
Chapel Street, Penzance, Cornwall TR18 4AF
Tel: 01736 363093

Real Ales, Bar Food, Restaurant Menu,
No Smoking Area, Disabled Facilities

99 Turnpike Inn
Turnpike Road, Connor Downs, Hayle,
Cornwall TR27 5DT
Tel: 01736 752377

Real Ales, Bar Food, Restaurant Menu,
No Smoking Area, Disabled Facilities

100 Union Hotel
Chapel Street, Penzance, Cornwall TR18 4AE
Tel: 01736 362319

Real Ales, Bar Food, Restaurant Menu,
Accommodation, No Smoking Area

101 Union Inn
Fore Street, St Ives, Cornwall TR26 1AB
Tel: 01736 796486

Real Ales, Bar Food

102 Watermill
Old Coach Road, Lelant Downs, Hayle,
Cornwall TR27 6LQ
Tel: 01736 757912

Real Ales, Bar Food, Restaurant Menu,
No Smoking Area

103 Wellington Hotel
Market Square, St Just, Cornwall TR19 7HD
Tel: 01736 787319

Real Ales, Bar Food, Restaurant Menu,
Accommodation, No Smoking Area

See panel below

103 The Wellington Hotel
Market Square, St Just, nr Penzance,
Cornwall TR19 7HD

☎ 01736 787319

🌐 www.wellington-hotel.co.uk

Real Ales, Bar Food, Restaurant Menu,
Accommodation, No Smoking Area

☛   Off the market place in St Just, 6 miles N of
Penzance on the A3071

🍺   Selection

🍴   Lunch and dinner

🛏   11 en suite rooms

💳   Major cards except Amex

🕐   Lunch and dinner

🏛   Penzance 6 miles

Built before the Battle of Waterloo in 1815, the handsome Wellington Hotel overlooks the market square in much-visited St Just. Fully modernised but retaining many period features, this friendly hotel has been run by Rod and Jennifer Gray since 1988. Highly regarded for its cooking, with plenty of local fish and shellfish, the Wellington is also a pleasant place to stay, with 11 well-appointed en suite bedrooms.

104 Welloe Rock Arms
Praa Sands, Nr Penzance, Cornwall TR20 9TQ
Tel: 01736 763516

Real Ales, Bar Food, Restaurant Menu,
No Smoking Area, Disabled Facilities

105 Western Hotel
Royal Square, Gabriel Street, St Ives,
Cornwall TR26 2ND
Tel: 01736 795277

Real Ales, Accommodation

106 White Hart Hotel
10 Foundry Square, Hayle, Cornwall TR27 4HQ
Tel: 01736 752322

Real Ales, Bar Food, Restaurant Menu,
Accommodation, No Smoking Area, Disabled Facilities

107 White Hart Inn
Ludgvan, Penzance, Cornwall TR20 8EY
Tel: 01736 740574

Real Ales, Bar Food, Restaurant Menu,
No Smoking Area, Disabled Facilities

108 Yacht Inn
The Promenade, Green Street, Penzance,
Cornwall TR18 4AU
Tel: 01736 362787

Real Ales, Bar Food, Restaurant Menu,
Accommodation, No Smoking Area, Disabled Facilities

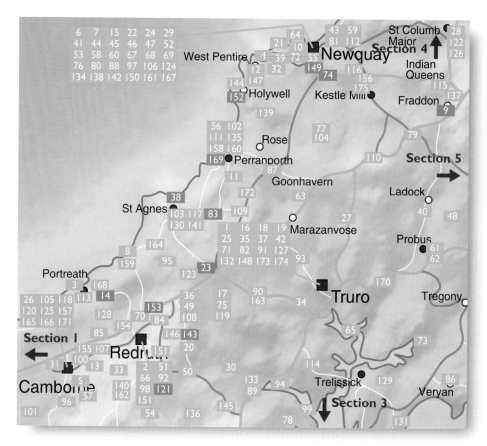

6	7	15	22	24	29
41	44	45	46	47	52
53	58	60	67	68	69
76	80	88	97	106	124
134	138	142	150	161	167

West Pentire

Newquay

St Columb 28
Major 122
Section 4 126

Indian
Queens

Holywell

Kestle Mill

Fraddon 137
9

Section 4

| 43 | 59 |
| 81 | 112 |

64	
21	10
39	72	55
32	
149	116
74	156
175	
115	

144 147
152
139

56	102
111	135
158	160
169	

Rose

Perranporth

Goonhavern

| 77 |
| 104 |

79

110

Section 5

Ladock

11
87

St Agnes

38

103 117 83
130 141

109

172

63

Marazanvose

| 40 |
| 48 |

27

Probus 61
62

1	16	18	19
25	35	37	42
71	82	91	127
132	148	173	174	93

8
164
159
95
23
123

Portreath

3 168

Truro

170

Tregony

26	105	118	113	14
120	125	157	
165	166	171	

128

85

Section 1

155 107
Redruth
151
20

Camborne

| 5 | |
| 96 | 57 |

140
162

98 121
151
54

101

36	17	90
49	75	163	34
108	119

153
70 84

146 143

30

65

73

133
89

94

Trelissick 129

Veryan 86

114

99

Section 3

78

131

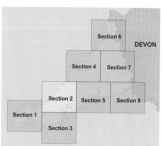

	Pub or Inn Reference Number - Detailed Information
11	Pub or Inn Reference Number - Detailed Information
12	Pub or Inn Reference Number - Summary Entry
●■	Place of interest mentioned in the chapter introduction

MID CORNWALL NORTH

Cornwall's chief holiday resort is Newquay, with superb beaches and many other leisure amenities. The crowning glory of Truro is its cathedral, completed as recently as 1910. History abounds here, in the lovely old towns of Redruth and Camborne, and in the former mining centre of St Agnes.

Camborne

A Town Trail guides visitors round this historic former mining town, taking in many interesting buildings and the **Geological Museum**. Outside the town's library stands a statue of Richard Trevethick, a native of Camborne and an inventor responsible for developing the high-pressure steam engine, the screw propeller and an early locomotive. He was also a formidable wrestler.

Newquay

Kestle Mill

West of the village is the handsome small Elizabethan manor house **Trerice**, an architectural gem standing in charming gardens and grounds. Among its more unusual attractions is the **Lawnmower Museum**.

Newquay

The old part of Newquay is centre round the harbour, which was for centuries busy with the pilchard fishing industry and the export of minerals and clay. The town is now Cornwall's chief holiday resort, with a beautiful rocky coastline and miles of golden sands. In fine weather the beaches and the surf are the main attractions, but at any time the town has plenty more to offer the visitor, including the **Blue Reef Aquarium**, **Waterworld** Leisure Park and a well-stocked **Zoo**.

Perranporth

A three-mile stretch of golden sands accounts for the popularity if this one-time

Perranporth

pilchard fishing and mining village as a holiday resort. A mile from the town, high up in the sand dunes, lies **St Pirran's Oratory**, built on the site of the grave of the eponymous Irish saint. Perranporth is closely linked with the author Winston Graham, who wrote the first volumes in the *Poldark* series while staying here.

Portreath

Now a thriving holiday centre, Portreath developed as a port exporting copper and importing coal. In 1809 the harbour was connected to the mines by the first railway in Cornwall, and the remains of the steep planed path can still be seen. To the south of Portreath lies the 250-acre **Tehidy Country Park** with nine miles of woodland walks. At Tolgus Mill, **Cornish Goldsmiths** has the largest collection of gold jewellery and artefacts in the West Country.

Probus

The granite tower of the **Church of St Probus and St Grace** is the grandest and tallest in all Cornwall, being an imposing 125 feet in height. The saints to whom the church is jointly dedicated were, most unusually, husband and wife. To the west of the village stands **Trewithen House**, an early Georgian building, and its glorious gardens, woods and parkland.

Redruth

Like many towns and villages in the area, Redruth prospered as a mining centre, and some fine Victorian, Georgian and earlier buildings remain as a legacy of those wealthy times. The countryside immediately to the south is dominated by the dramatic **Carn Brea**, whose summit is crowned by a 90ft monument to Francis Bassett, a local land and mine owner and benefactor.

St Agnes

The many mine workings around St Agnes include a group of buildings that were once part of the county's most famous mines – **Wheal Coates**. Nearby, the **Blue Hills Tin Stream Visitor Centre** perpetuates the skills of the tin workers. **St Agnes Museum**

Truro Cathedral

promotes the heritage of the area with a series of displays covering its mining and seafaring history and the natural history of the region. The **Craft Trail** passes a row of miners' cottages known as **Stippy Stappy** on its way down to Trevaunance Cove.

St Columb Major

This small village was once considered the site of Cornwall's cathedral, and its claims were not unfounded, as the parish **Church of St Columba** is on a grand scale. It contains some magnificent 16th and 17th century monumental brasses.

Trelissick

On a promontory bounded by the River Fal and two creeks, the **Trelissick Estate** is an 18 th century house set in 25 acres of lovely gardens and adjoined by 500 acres of park and farmland. Close to the Estate is the landing point of the **King Harry Ferry**, which takes cars and passengers across the narrow stretch of water between Feock on the west bank and Philleigh on the Roseland Peninsula.

Truro

The crowning glory of this small, elegant city is its Cathedral, built in the Early English style and completed as recently as 1910. Its collection of stained glass is one of the finest in England, and among other treasures are two 14th century statues that came from Brittany. The **Royal Cornwall Museum** explores the history of the county from the Stone Age to the present day, while in the Art Gallery are works by Constable and Lowry as well as the Newlyn School of Artists.

1   The Admiral Boscawen

7 Richmond Hill Approach, Truro,
Cornwall TR1 3HS
Tel: 01872 278941

Real Ales, Bar Food, No Smoking Area,
Disabled Facilities

2   The Basset Arms

51 Fore Street, Redruth, Cornwall TR15 3DY
Tel: 01209 612320

Real Ales, Bar Food, Restaurant Menu,
Accommodation, No Smoking Area

3   Basset Arms

Tregea Terrace, Portreath, Redruth,
Cornwall TR16 4NG
Tel: 01209 842077

Real Ales, Bar Food, No Smoking Area

4   The Bay Hotel

Esplanade Rd, Newquay, Cornwall TR7 1PT
Tel: 01637 852221

Real Ales, Restaurant Menu, Accommodation,
No Smoking Area, Disabled Facilities

5   The Beacon Inn

80 Fore Street, Beacon, Camborne,
Cornwall TR14 7SE
Tel: 01209 717950

Real Ales

6   Belushis

35 Fore St, Newquay, Cornwall TR7 1HD
Tel: 01637 859111

Bar Food, Restaurant Menu, Accommodation,
No Smoking Area, Disabled Facilities

7   Beresford Hotel

Narrowcliff, Newquay, Cornwall TR7 2PR
Tel: 01637 873238

Restaurant Menu, Accommodation, No Smoking Area,
Disabled Facilities

8   Blue

Beach Rd, Porthtowan, Truro, Cornwall TR4 8AA
Tel: 01209 890329

Bar Food, Restaurant Menu, Disabled Facilities

9   Blue Anchor Inn

Fraddon, StColumb, Cornwall TR9 6LS
Tel: 01726 860352

Real Ales, Bar Food

See panel below

9   The Blue Anchor Inn

Fraddon, nr St Columb Major, Cornwall TR9 6LS
☎ 01726 860352

Real Ales, Bar Food

☞ On the newly created Trafalgar Way in the village of Fraddon just off the A30 south of the Indian Queens junction

🍺 St Austell Tribute and Tinners

🍴 12-2 & 6.30-9.30

♫ Live music last Saturday of the month

⛰ Garden, patio, car park

💳 Major cards

🕐 11-3 & 6-11 (all day Friday, Saturday, Sunday)

🏛 Indian Queens Screech Owl Sanctuary 1 mile, Trerice (NT) 3 miles, Newquay 7 miles

Situated on the newly created Trafalgar Way, the **Blue Anchor** has been run for 25 years by John and Mary Rickard. Their hospitality has won them many friends, and Mary's cooking is another very good reason for the inn's popularity. Her steak & kidney pie is justly renowned, and a glass of St Austell's ale is the perfect accompaniment.

10   The Boarding House

32 Headland Rd, Newquay, Cornwall TR7 1HN
Tel: 01637 873258

Restaurant Menu, Accommodation, No Smoking Area

11   Bolingey Inn

Penwartha Rd, Bolingey , Perranporth,
Cornwall TR6 0DH
Tel: 01872 572794

Real Ales, Bar Food, Restaurant Menu,
Disabled Facilities

12 Bowgie Inn

West Pentire Road, Crantock, Newquay,
Cornwall TR8 5SE
Tel: 01637 830363
Real Ales, Bar Food, Restaurant Menu,
Disabled Facilities

13 Brea Inn and Restaurant

Higher Brea, Camborne, Cornwall TR14 9DA
Tel: 01209 713706
Real Ales, Bar Food, Restaurant Menu,
No Smoking Area, Disabled Facilities

14 Bridge Inn

Bridge, Cornwall TR16 4OW
Tel: 01209 842532
Real Ales, Bar Food, Restaurant Menu,
No Smoking Area, Disabled Facilities

See panel below

15 Bristol Hotel

Narrowcliff, Newquay, Cornwall TR7 2PQ
Tel: 01637 875181
Bar Food, Restaurant Menu, Accommodation,
No Smoking Area

16 Britannia Inn

Quay Street, Truro, Cornwall TR1 2HE
Tel: 01872 273700
Real Ales, Bar Food, Restaurant Menu,
No Smoking Area

17 Britannia Inn

Fore Street, Chacewater, Truro, Cornwall TR4 8PY
Tel: 01872 560362
Real Ales, Bar Food, Restaurant Menu,
No Smoking Area, Disabled Facilities

14 The Bridge Inn

Bridge, nr Portreath, Cornwall TR16 4OW
☎ 01209 642532

**Real Ales, Bar Food, Restaurant Menu,
No Smoking Area, Disabled Facilities**

☞ The inn lies 5 miles off the A30 west of
Redruth on the B3300 road to Portreath

🍺 Sharp's, Greene King IPA

🍴 Home cooking incl. seafood specials

🎵 Weekly quiz

⚓ Car park, beer garden by stream

💳 Major cards

🕐 12-3 & 6-11

🏛 Portreath 1 mile, Redruth 5 miles

The oldest pub in the village of Bridge is
also one of the most hospitable in the
region. In a steep wooded valley near
Portreath, **The Bridge Inn** dates back to the
17th century, when it was a hunting lodge,
and the many original features create a really
delightful, traditional ambience.

Lovers of real ales are in their element here,
and in the newly opened non-smoking
restaurant good honest home-cooked food is
served lunchtime and evening.

The choice includes pasta, pizza, fresh fish
from Newlyn and popular classics such as
cauliflower cheese, steak & ale pie, ham, egg &
chips, Cornish pasties, chilli con carne and
braised lamb shanks. The Bridge Inn has plenty
of parking, and in warm weather the tables
outside in the garden by a stream really come
into their own.

18 Brookdale Hotel
Tregolls Road, Truro, Cornwall TR1 1JZ
Tel: 01872 273513
Real Ales, Bar Food, Accommodation,
No Smoking Area, Disabled Facilities

19 Bunters Bar
58 Little Castle St, Truro, Cornwall TR1 3DL
Tel: 01872 241220
Real Ales, No Smoking Area, Disabled Facilities

20 Carharrack Stars Inn
Fore Street, Carharrack, Redruth,
Cornwall TR16 5QS
Tel: 01209 820295
Real Ales, Bar Food, No Smoking Area,
Disabled Facilities

21 Carnmarth Hotel
Headland Road, Fistral Beach, Newquay,
Cornwall TR7 1HN
Tel: 01637 872519
Bar Food, Accommodation, Disabled Facilities

22 Central Inn
11 Central Square, Newquay, Cornwall TR7 1EU
Tel: 01637 873810
Real Ales, Bar Food, Restaurant Menu,
No Smoking Area, Disabled Facilities

23 Chiverton Arms
Chiverton Cross, Blackwater, St Agnes,
Cornwall TR4 8HS
Tel: 01872 560240
Real Ales, Bar Food, Restaurant Menu,
Accommodation, No Smoking Area, Disabled Facilities
See panel below

---

23 The Chiverton Arms
Chiverton Cross, Blackwater, nr St Agnes,
Cornwall TR4 8HS
☎ 01872 560240
🔲 www.chivertonarms.co.uk

Real Ales, Bar Food, Restaurant Menu, Accommodation, No Smoking Area, Disabled Facilities

☛ Blackwater lies just off the A30 3 miles north of Redruth

🍺 Sharp's and guests

🍴 Wide variety of home cooking

🛏 4 rooms (incl. 2 family rooms)

⛱ Garden, car park

💳 Major Cards

🕐 11-10

🏛 St Agnes 3 miles, Redruth 3 miles, Truro 6 miles

In a fine old inn dating from 1780, Julia and Roger offer a warm welcome, excellent accommodation, good food and a wide selection of drinks including Cornish real ales and wines by glass or bottle. The restaurant at

The Chiverton Arms has recently been refurbished and extended to provide a very stylish setting for enjoying home cooking that includes fresh fish specials, classics such as steak & kidney pie and liver & bacon, and some very tempting puddings. Picnic tables are set out in the delightful lawned beer garden. The four guest bedrooms in an adjacent building, all with en suite showers, include two that are suitable for families. The inn is close to many attractions both country and coastal, and the proximity of the A30 provides easy access to further flung places of interest.

24 Chy An Mor
12 Beach Road, Newquay, Cornwall TR7 1ES
Tel: 01637 873415
Bar Food, Restaurant Menu, No Smoking Area,
Disabled Facilities

25 City Inn
Pydar Street, Truro, Cornwall TR1 3SP
Tel: 01872 272623
Real Ales, Bar Food, Restaurant Menu,
Accommodation, No Smoking Area, Disabled Facilities

26 The Clipper Bar
9 Commercial Street, Camborne,
Cornwall TR14 8JZ
Tel: 01209 612656
Real Ales, Disabled Facilities

27 The Clock and Key
Trispen, Truro, Cornwall TR4 9AZ
Tel: 01872 279626
Real Ales, Bar Food, Restaurant Menu,
No Smoking Area, Disabled Facilities

28 The Coaching Inn
13 Bank Street, St Columb, Cornwall TR9 6AT
Tel: 01637 881408
Real Ales, Disabled Facilities

29 Corkers
5 Beach Rd, Newquay, Cornwall TR7 1ES
Tel: 01637 878666
Bar Food, No Smoking Area, Disabled Facilities

30 Cornish Arms
Frogpool, Truro, Cornwall TR4 8RP
Tel: 01872 863445
Real Ales, Bar Food, Disabled Facilities

31 The Cornish Choughs
Treswithian, Camborne, Cornwall TR14 7NW
Tel: 01209 712361
Real Ales, Bar Food, Restaurant Menu,
No Smoking Area, Disabled Facilities

32 Cornishman
Langurroc Rd, Crantock, Newquay,
Cornwall TR8 5RB
Tel: 01637 830869
Real Ales, Bar Food, Restaurant Menu,
No Smoking Area, Disabled Facilities

33 The Countryman
Piece, Carnkie, Redruth, Cornwall TR16 6SG
Tel: 01209 215960
Real Ales, Bar Food, Restaurant Menu,
Disabled Facilities

34 County Arms
Highertown, Truro, Cornwall TR1 3PY
Tel: 01872 273972
Real Ales, Bar Food, Restaurant Menu,
No Smoking Area, Disabled Facilities

35 Crab and Ale House
New Bridge Street, Truro, Cornwall TR1 2AA
Tel: 01872 277294
Real Ales, Bar Food, Restaurant Menu,
No Smoking Area, Disabled Facilities

36 Crossroads Hotel
Scorrier, Redruth, Cornwall TR16 5BP
Tel: 01209 820551
Real Ales, Bar Food, Restaurant Menu,
Accommodation, No Smoking Area, Disabled Facilities

37 Daniell Arms
Infirmary Hill, Truro, Cornwall TR1 2JA
Tel: 01872 271037
Real Ales, Disabled Facilities

38 Driftwood Spars Hotel
Quay Road, Trevaunance Cove, St Agnes,
Cornwall TR5 0RT
Tel: 01872 552428
Real Ales, Bar Food, Restaurant Menu,
Accommodation, No Smoking Area, Disabled Facilities
See panel on page 28

38 The Driftwood Spars Hotel

Trevaunance Cove, St Agnes, Cornwall TR5 0RT
☎ 01872 552428/553323
🌐 www.driftwoodspars.com

Real Ales, Bar Food, Restaurant Menu, Accommodation, No Smoking Area, Disabled Facilities

- ☞ On the coast a short walk from St Agnes
- 🍺 Own brew produced on site
- ▌ 12-2.30 & 6.30-9.30
- 🛏 15 en suite rooms
- ⚒ Garden, car park
- 💳 Major cards accepted
- 🕐 All day
- 🏛 Blue Hills ½ mile, Wheal Coates 1 mile, St Agnes ½ mile, Truro 8 miles

Built as a marine warehouse and fish cellar, the Driftwood Spars Hotel was converted to its current role in the 1930s. Dating from 1660, the construction materials included Cornish slate and granite and timbers made from massive ships' spars. The result of sensitive renovation and modernisation is 15 excellent en suite bedrooms and a series of bars and restaurants that combine comfort and character at a very high level. The hotel fully deserves its motto 'a little bit different' and guests quickly feel at home in this very special hotel run for more than 20 years by Jill and Gordon Treleaven and family. Open throughout the year, the Driftwood Spars has bars and eating areas on two levels offering an impressive variety of drinks and freshly prepared food using local produce. Also on the premises are a gift shop and a microbrewery. The hotel sits close to the beach in an area that provides the visitor with miles of wonderful coastline and unsurpassed views.

39 The Esplanade Hotel

9 Esplanade Road, Pentire, Newquay,
Cornwall TR7 1PS
Tel: 01637 873333

Real Ales, Bar Food, Restaurant Menu,
Accommodation, No Smoking Area, Disabled Facilities

40 Falmouth Arms

Ladock, Truro, Cornwall TR2 4PG
Tel: 01726 882319

Real Ales, Bar Food, Restaurant Menu, No Smoking
Area, Disabled Facilities

41 Famous Firkin

48 Porthbean Road, Newquay, Cornwall TR7 1HS
Tel: 01637 875753

Real Ales

42 The Famous Old Globe

Frances Street, Truro, Cornwall TR1 3DP
Tel: 01872 273869

Real Ales, Bar Food, Restaurant Menu,
No Smoking Area, Disabled Facilities

43 Farmers Arms

Church Street, St Columb Minor, Newquay,
Cornwall TR7 3EZ
Tel: 01637 872277

Real Ales, Bar Food, Restaurant Menu,
No Smoking Area

44 Fistral Bay Hotel

1 Pentire Avenue, Newquay, Cornwall TR7 1NT
Tel: 01637 874277

Restaurant Menu, Accommodation, No Smoking Area,
Disabled Facilities

45 Fistral Beach Hotel
13 Esplanade Rd, Newquay, Cornwall TR7 1QA
Tel: 01637 850626

Bar Food, Accommodation, Disabled Facilities

46 The Fistral Inn
1 Pentire Avenue, Newquay, Cornwall TR7 1NT
Tel: 01637 874027

Disabled Facilities

47 The Fort Inn
63 Fore Street, Newquay, Cornwall TR7 1HA
Tel: 01637 875700

Real Ales, Bar Food, No Smoking Area,
Disabled Facilities

48 The Four Burrows
The Square, Grampound Road, Truro,
Cornwall TR2 4DT
Tel: 01726 882296

Real Ales, Disabled Facilities

49 Fox and Hounds
Scorrier, Redruth, Cornwall TR16 5BS
Tel: 01209 820205

Real Ales, Bar Food, Restaurant Menu,
No Smoking Area, Disabled Facilities

50 Fox and Hounds Public House
Comford, Redruth, Cornwall TR16 6AX
Tel: 01209 820251

Real Ales, Bar Food, Restaurant Menu,
No Smoking Area, Disabled Facilities

51 Gaslights
Station Hill, Redruth, Cornwall TR15 2PP
Tel: 01209 218393

Bar Food, Restaurant Menu, Accommodation,
No Smoking Area

52 Glendorgal Hotel
Lusty Glaze Road, Newquay, Cornwall TR7 3AB
Tel: 01637 874937

Bar Food, Restaurant Menu, Accommodation,
No Smoking Area

53 Godolphin Arms Hotel
86-88 Henver Rd, Newquay, Cornwall TR7 3BL
Tel: 01637 872572

Real Ales, Bar Food, Restaurant Menu,
Accommodation, No Smoking Area, Disabled Facilities

54 Golden Lion Inn
Stithians Lake, Menhenion, Nr Redruth,
Cornwall TR16 6NW
Tel: 01209 860332

Real Ales, Bar Food, Restaurant Menu,
No Smoking Area, Disabled Facilities

55 Great Western Hotel
Cliff Road, Newquay, Cornwall TR7 2PT
Tel: 01637 872010

Real Ales, Bar Food, Accommodation,
No Smoking Area, Disabled Facilities

56 The Green Parrot
Perranporth, Cornwall TR6 0JP
Tel: 01872 573284

Real Ales, Bar Food, Restaurant Menu,
No Smoking Area, Disabled Facilities

57 Grenville Arms
Fore Street, Troon, Camborne, Cornwall TR14 9EF
Tel: 01209 712541

58 The Griffin
3 5 Cliff Road, Newquay, Cornwall TR7 1SP
Tel: 01637 874067

Real Ales, Bar Food, Restaurant Menu,
Accommodation, No Smoking Area, Disabled Facilities

59 Gull Rock Hotel
Watergate Rd, Porth, Newquay, Cornwall TR7 3LX
Tel: 01637 873482

Accommodation, No Smoking Area

60 The Harbour Hotel
North Quay Hill, Newquay, Cornwall TR7 1HF
Tel: 01637 873040

Bar Food, Restaurant Menu, Accommodation,
No Smoking Area

74 The Kings Head

Lane, Newquay, Cornwall TR8 4QB
☎ 01637 876666

Real Ales, Bar Food, Restaurant Menu,
No Smoking Area, Disabled Facilities

- 2 miles from Newquay, where the A392 meets the A3075
- HSD, Tribute
- 12-9.30
- Live music Thursday from 8.30
- Beer garden, large car park opposite
- Major cards except Amex
- All day
- Trerice 1 mile, Newquay 2 miles

On the roundabout at Lane, where the A392 meets the A3075, the **Kings Head** is easy to spot with its distinctive, steeply raked roof and attractive dormer window. When Ick

and Claire Walters came here in the spring of 2004 to manage the pub, it was not in the best of health, but with their experience, enthusiasm and hard work they have restored its fortunes and made it a real winner, with a loyal and growing following.

Just a short drive from Newquay, and easily reached from the main A30 route into Cornwall, the inn is very popular both with local residents and with the tourists who visit this part of the world throughout the year. The main attraction is the excellent food

served here all day in the cheerful bar, in the non-smoking restaurant or outside in the garden, which has a barbecue area. The menus provide a good choice for all tastes and appetites, and the carvery, available from 5 to 9.30 and all day Thursday to Sunday, is a very popular feature.

Three real ales – Skinners Tribute, HSD and a rotating guest from the St Austell Brewery, are on tap to quench thirsts or to accompany the very enjoyable food. Always a very friendly, relaxing place, the Kings Head has a warm welcome for all the family – and their dogs! These qualities make it a pub well worth seeking out, as a destination for a drink and a meal, or as a break for refreshment while visiting the local sights, which include the lovely coast, the numerous attractions of Newquay and local places of interest such as the National Trust's Trerice, a gem of a small Elizabethan manor house. Claire also has an interest in The Tavern at Treninnick (qv), equally well known for its hospitality and good food and drink.

61 Hawkins Arms
Probus, Truro, Cornwall TR2 4JL
Tel: 01726 882208

Real Ales, Bar Food, Restaurant Menu,
Accommodation, No Smoking Area

62 The Hawkins Arms
Fore Street, Probus, Cornwall TR2 4JL
Tel: 01726 882208

Real Ales, Bar Food, Restaurant Menu,
Accommodation, No Smoking Area

63 Hawkins Arms
High Street, Zelah, Truro, Cornwall TR4 9HU
Tel: 01872 540339

Real Ales, Bar Food, No Smoking Area

64 Headland Hotel
Fistral Beach, Newquay, Cornwall TR7 1EW
Tel: 01637 872211

Real Ales, Bar Food, Restaurant Menu,
Accommodation, No Smoking Area, Disabled Facilities

65 Heron Inn
Trenhaile Terrace, Malpas, Truro, Cornwall TR1 1SL
Tel: 01872 272773

Real Ales, Bar Food, Restaurant Menu,
No Smoking Area, Disabled Facilities

66 The Hollies Hotel
Penryn St, Redruth, Cornwall TR15 2SP
Tel: 01209 214987

Real Ales, Bar Food, Restaurant Menu,
Accommodation, No Smoking Area, Disabled Facilities

67 Hotel California
Pentire Crescent, Newquay, Cornwall TR7 1PU
Tel: 01637 872798

Bar Food, Restaurant Menu, Accommodation,
No Smoking Area, Disabled Facilities

68 Hotel Riviera
1 Lusty Glaze Road, Newquay, Cornwall TR73AA
Tel: 01637 874251

Real Ales, Bar Food, Restaurant Menu,
Accommodation, No Smoking Area, Disabled Facilities

69 Hotel Victoria
East St, Newquay, Cornwall TR7 1DB
Tel: 01637 872255

Bar Food, No Smoking Area, Disabled Facilities

70 The Inn For All Seasons
Treleigh, Redruth, Cornwall TR16 4AP
Tel: 01209 219511

Real Ales, Bar Food, Restaurant Menu,
No Smoking Area, Disabled Facilities

71 Kazbah
3 Quay St, Truro, Cornwall TR1 2HB
Tel: 01872 272276

Real Ales, Bar Food, Disabled Facilities

72 Key West Hotel
117 Mount Wise, Newquay, Cornwall TR7 1QR
Tel: 01637 873155

Restaurant Menu, Accommodation, No Smoking Area

73 Kings Head
Ruan Lanihorne, Nr Tregony, Cornwall TR2 5NX
Tel: 01872 501263

Real Ales, Bar Food, Restaurant Menu,
No Smoking Area, Disabled Facilities

74 Kings Head
Kings Head Lane, Newquay, Cornwall TR8 4QB
Tel: 01637 876666

Real Ales, Bar Food, Restaurant Menu,
No Smoking Area, Disabled Facilities

See panel opposite

75 Kings Head Inn
The Square, Chacewater, Truro, Cornwall TR4 8PY
Tel: 01872 560652

Real Ales, Bar Food, Restaurant Menu,
No Smoking Area, Disabled Facilities

76 Lanherne Pub and Restaurant
32 Ulalia Road, Newquay, Cornwall TR7 2PZ
Tel: 01637 872308

Real Ales, Bar Food, Restaurant Menu,
No Smoking Area, Disabled Facilities

83 The Miners Arms

Mithian, nr St Agnes, Cornwall TR5 0QF
☎ 01872 552375

Real Ales, Bar Food, Restaurant Menu,
No Smoking Area

- 🐾 2 miles E of St Agnes off the B3284 or B3285
- 🍺 Doom Bar + guests
- 🍴 12-3 & 6-9
- 🎵 Folk bands twice a month
- ⛫ Garden front and rear, car park
- 💳 Major cards except Amex and Diners
- 🕐 11-11 (Sun 12-10.30)
- 🏛 St Agnes 2 miles, Perranporth 3 miles

One of the oldest buildings in Mithian, the Miners Arms served the community when the village was at the centre of the business of extracting minerals from the earth. In its long history it has been a chapel, a mine-

owner's office and a private residence, and in its present role it provides outstanding hospitality and superb food and drink to the village and surrounding area, and also to the many visitors who come to explore this part of the world every year.

It's the first venture into this field for Chris and Dee, who came here in February 2005 and have already made many friends. The inn is full of interest and atmosphere, and the long and fascinating history is reflected in priest holes, ghosts, a secret

tunnel, period photographs and paintings of historical characters with local connections. The back bar features a beamed and planked ceiling and a woodblock floor, and another room has the feel of an old-fashioned sitting room. A wonderfully atmospheric cellar dining area has tables squeezed between white-painted rough stone walls.

The long main bar serves an excellent range of drinks, with Sharps Doom Bar heading the real ales, and when the weather is kind the inn's two outside seating areas come into their own: picnic benches are set out on the cobbled forecourt, and at the back is a paved area with lots of flowers and greenery, garden furniture and patio heaters. The Miners Arms offers a great choice of outstanding bar and restaurant food, from ciabattas with mouthwatering fillings like steak & stilton to scrumptious dishes typified by crab cakes, chicken Wellington, steak & ale pie, rack of Cornish lamb and cider-poached tuna presented on a pesto mash. Wines from around the world complement the fine food.

77 Lanine Hotel
Cargoll Rd, Newlyn East, Newquay,
Cornwall TR8 5LB
Tel: 01872 510223
Disabled Facilities

78 Lemon Arms
Lemon Hill, Mylor Bridge, Falmouth,
Cornwall TR11 5NA
Tel: 01326 373666
Real Ales, Bar Food, Restaurant Menu,
No Smoking Area, Disabled Facilities

79 London Inn
School Road, Summercourt, Newquay,
Cornwall TR8 5EA
Tel: 01872 510281
Real Ales, Bar Food, Restaurant Menu

80 Mavericks
70 Henver Road, Newquay, Cornwall TR7 3BN
Tel: 01637 878089
Real Ales, Bar Food, Restaurant Menu,
Accommodation, No Smoking Area

81 Mermaid Inn
Alexandra Road, Porth, Newquay,
Cornwall TR7 3NB
Tel: 01637 872954
Real Ales, Bar Food, Restaurant Menu,
No Smoking Area

82 The Mi Bar
Lemon Quay, Truro, Cornwall TR1 2LL
Tel: 01872 277214
Real Ales, Bar Food, Restaurant Menu

83 The Miners Arms
Mithian, St Agnes, Cornwall TR5 0QF
Tel: 01872 552375
Real Ales, Bar Food, Restaurant Menu,
No Smoking Area
See panel opposite

84 Mount Ambrose Inn
Mount Ambrose, Redruth, Cornwall TR15 1QR
Tel: 01209 218124
Real Ales

85 New Inn
St Johns Terrace, Redruth, Cornwall TR15 3UF
Tel: 01209 216262
Real Ales, Bar Food, Restaurant Menu,
No Smoking Area, Disabled Facilities

86 The New Inn
Veryan In Roseland, Truro, Cornwall TR2 5QA
Tel: 01872 501362
Real Ales, Bar Food, Restaurant Menu,
Accommodation, No Smoking Area, Disabled Facilities

87 The New Inn
Newquay Rd, Goonhavern, Truro,
Cornwall TR4 9QD
Tel: 01872 573326
Real Ales, Bar Food, Restaurant Menu,
No Smoking Area, Disabled Facilities

88 Newquay Arms
Bank Street, Newquay, Cornwall TR7 1JF
Tel: 01637 878887
Restaurant Menu, No Smoking Area

89 The Norway Inn
Perranwharf, Perranworthal, Truro,
Cornwall TR3 7NU
Tel: 01872 864241
Real Ales, Bar Food, Restaurant Menu,
No Smoking Area, Disabled Facilities

90 Oak Tree Inn
Threemilestone, Truro, Cornwall TR3 6BU
Tel: 01872 278479
Real Ales, Bar Food, Restaurant Menu,
No Smoking Area

91 Old Ale House
7 Quay Street, Truro, Cornwall TR1 2HD
Tel: 01872 271122
Real Ales, Bar Food, Restaurant Menu,
No Smoking Area, Disabled Facilities

92 The Old Coach House
34 Fore St, Redruth, Cornwall TR15 2AE
Tel: 01209 215416
Real Ales, Bar Food, No Smoking Area

93 The Old Plough Inn
Church Rd , Shortlanesend, Truro,
Cornwall TR4 9DY
Tel: 01872 273001

Real Ales, Bar Food, Restaurant Menu,
No Smoking Area, Disabled Facilities

94 Old Quay Inn
St Johns Terrace, Devoran, Truro,
Cornwall TR3 6ND
Tel: 01872 863142

Real Ales, Bar Food, No Smoking Area

95 Old School
Mount Hawke, Truro, Cornwall TR4 8BA
Tel: 01209 891158

Real Ales, Bar Food, Restaurant Menu,
No Smoking Area, Disabled Facilities

96 The Old Shire Inn
Pendarves Road, Camborne, Cornwall TR14 0RT
Tel: 01209 712691

Real Ales, Bar Food, Restaurant Menu,
No Smoking Area, Disabled Facilities

97 On The Rocks
14 The Cresent, Newquay, Cornwall TR7 1DT
Tel: 01637 872897

Bar Food

98 The Oxford Inn
28 Fore Street, Redruth, Cornwall TR15 2BQ
Tel: 01209 215651

Real Ales, No Smoking Area, Disabled Facilities

99 Pandora Inn
Restronguet Creek, Mylor Bridge, Falmouth,
Cornwall TR11 5ST
Tel: 01326 372678

Real Ales, Bar Food, Restaurant Menu,
No Smoking Area, Disabled Facilities

100 Pendarves Arms
20 Pendarves Street, Camborne,
Cornwall TR14 8RF
Tel: 01209 612775

Real Ales, Disabled Facilities

101 Pendarves Inn
Carnhell Green, Nr Camborne,
Cornwall TR14 0NB
Tel: 01209 832116

Real Ales, Bar Food, Restaurant Menu,
Accommodation, No Smoking Area, Disabled Facilities

102 The Perranporth Hotel
St Pirans Rd, Perranporth, Cornwall TR6 0BJ
Tel: 01872 573234

Real Ales, Bar Food, Restaurant Menu,
Accommodation

103 Peterville Inn
Peterville, St Agnes, Cornwall TR5 0QU
Tel: 01872 552406

Real Ales, Bar Food, Restaurant Menu,
Accommodation, No Smoking Area

104 Pheasant Inn
Church Town, Newlyn East, Nr Newquay,
Cornwall TR8 5LJ
Tel: 01872 510237

Real Ales, Bar Food, Restaurant Menu,
No Smoking Area

105 The Plough Inn
7 College St, Camborne, Cornwall TR14 7JU
Tel: 01209 711065

Real Ales, Accommodation

106 The Plum Tree
19 Bank St, Newquay, Cornwall TR7 1DH
Tel: 01637 872814

Bar Food, Restaurant Menu, No Smoking Area

107 Plume Of Feathers
Fore Street, Pool, Redruth, Cornwall TR15 3PF
Tel: 01209 713513

Real Ales, Bar Food, Restaurant Menu,
No Smoking Area, Disabled Facilities

108 Plume Of Feathers
Scorrier, Redruth, Cornwall TR16 5BN
Tel: 01209 822002

Real Ales

109 Plume Of Feathers

Penhallow, Truro, Cornwall TR4 9LT
Tel: 01872 571389

Real Ales, Bar Food, Restaurant Menu,
No Smoking Area, Disabled Facilities

110 Plume Of Feathers

Mitchell, Truro, Cornwall TR8 5AX
Tel: 01872 510387

Real Ales, Bar Food, Restaurant Menu,
Accommodation, No Smoking Area, Disabled Facilities

111 Ponsmere Hotel

Ponsmere Road, Perranporth, Cornwall TR6 0BW
Tel: 01872 572225

Real Ales, Bar Food, Accommodation,
No Smoking Area, Disabled Facilities

112 Porth Lodge Hotel

Porth Bean Rd, Newquay, Cornwall TR7 3LT
Tel: 01637 874483

Real Ales, Bar Food, Restaurant Menu,
Accommodation, No Smoking Area

113 Portreath Arms Hotel

The Square , Portreath, Redruth,
Cornwall TR16 4LA
Tel: 01209 842259

Real Ales, Bar Food, Restaurant Menu,
Accommodation, No Smoking Area, Disabled Facilities

114 Punch Bowl and Ladle

Penelewey Creek, Feock, Truro, Cornwall TR3 6QY
Tel: 01872 862237

Real Ales, Bar Food, Restaurant Menu,
No Smoking Area, Disabled Facilities

115 Queen and Railway Inn

St Columb Road, St Columb, Cornwall TR9 6QR
Tel: 01726 860343

Real Ales

116 Quintrell Inn

2 North Way, Quintrell, Newquay,
Cornwall TR8 4LA
Tel: 01637 874427

Real Ales, Bar Food, Restaurant Menu,
No Smoking Area, Disabled Facilities

117 Railway Inn

10 Vicarage Road, St Agnes, Cornwall TR5 0TJ
Tel: 01872 552310

Real Ales, Bar Food, Restaurant Menu,
No Smoking Area, Disabled Facilities

118 The Railway Tavern

Trevu Rd, Camborne, Cornwall TR14 8SR
Tel: 01209 712389

Real Ales, Bar Food

119 Rambling Minor

High Street, Chacewater, Truro, Cornwall TR4 8LU
Tel: 01872 560238

Real Ales, Bar Food, Restaurant Menu,
No Smoking Area, Disabled Facilities

121 The Red Lion

35 Fore Street, Redruth, Cornwall TR15 2 AE
☎ 01209 216348

**Real Ales, Bar Food, Restaurant Menu,
Accommodation**

☛ Just off the A393 in the centre of Redruth

🍺 Local brews

🍴 12.15-2 & 5-8

🛏 2 en suite rooms

🎵 Live music Thurs, disco Fri & Sat, karaoke Sun

🕐 11-11 (Sun 12-10.30)

🏛 Attractions of Redruth; Camborne 2 miles, Gwennap 2 miles

Window boxes and hanging baskets make a colourful show at the **Red Lion**, where Carole and her parents Jenny and Keith welcome visitors. The fully stocked bar features four real ales, and Jenny's menu tempts with a fine selection of hot and cold home-cooked food every lunchtime and dinner. On the main street of Redruth, the convivial Red Lion has two en suite rooms that provide a pleasant base for exploring Redruth and the surrounding area.

120 Red Jacket Tavern
66 Trevenson Street, Camborne,
Cornwall TR14 8HZ
Tel: 01209 712682
Bar Food, Disabled Facilities

121 **Red Lion**
Fore Street, Redruth, Cornwall TR15 2AE
Tel: 01209 216348
Real Ales, Bar Food, Restaurant Menu,
Accommodation
See panel on page 35

122 The Red Lion Hotel
44 Fore St, StColumb, Cornwall TR9 6RH
Tel: 01637 880408
Real Ales, Restaurant Menu, Accommodation,
No Smoking Area, Disabled Facilities

123 Red Lion Inn
Blackwater, Truro, Cornwall TR4 8EU
Tel: 01872 560289
Real Ales, Bar Food, Restaurant Menu,
No Smoking Area, Disabled Facilities

124 Red Lion Inn
North Quay Hill, Newquay, Cornwall TR7 1HE
Tel: 01637 872195
Real Ales, Bar Food, Restaurant Menu,
No Smoking Area, Disabled Facilities

125 Regal Hotel
2 Church Lane, Camborne, Cornwall TR14 7DH
Tel: 01209 713131
Real Ales, Bar Food, Restaurant Menu,
Accommodation, No Smoking Area

126 Ring O'Bells
3 Bank Street, St Columb Major, Newquay,
Cornwall TR9 6AT
Tel: 01637 880259
Real Ales, Bar Food, Restaurant Menu,
No Smoking Area

127 Rising Sun Inn
Mitchell Hill, Truro, Cornwall TR1 1ED
Tel: 01872 273454
Real Ales, Bar Food, No Smoking Area,
Disabled Facilities

128 The Robartes Arms
Robartes Terrace, Redruth, Cornwall TR16 4RX
Tel: 01209 842280
Real Ales, Bar Food, Restaurant Menu,
No Smoking Area, Disabled Facilities

129 The Roseland Inn
Philleigh, Truro, Cornwall TR2 5NB
Tel: 01872 580254
Real Ales, Bar Food, Restaurant Menu,
No Smoking Area

130 Rosemundy House Hotel
Rosemundy Hill, St Agnes, Cornwall TR5 0UF
Tel: 01872 552101
Bar Food, Restaurant Menu, Accommodation,
No Smoking Area, Disabled Facilities

131 Rosevine Hotel
Rosevine , Portscatho, Truro, Cornwall TR2 5EW
Tel: 01872 580206
Real Ales, Bar Food, Restaurant Menu,
Accommodation, No Smoking Area, Disabled Facilities

132 Royal Hotel
Lemon Street, Truro, Cornwall TR1 2QB
Tel: 01872 270345
Real Ales, Bar Food, Accommodation,
No Smoking Area, Disabled Facilities

133 Royal Oak
Perranwell Station, Truro, Cornwall TR3 7PX
Tel: 01872 863175
Real Ales, Bar Food, Restaurant Menu,
No Smoking Area, Disabled Facilities

134 Sandy Lodge Hotel
8-12 Hillgrove Rd, Newquay, Cornwall TR7 2QY
Tel: 01637 872851
Bar Food, Restaurant Menu, Accommodation,
No Smoking Area

135 The Seiners Arms
Beach Road, Perranporth, Cornwall TR6 0DP
Tel: 01872 573118
Real Ales, Bar Food, Restaurant Menu,
Accommodation, No Smoking Area, Disabled Facilities

136 Seven Stars Inn
Church Road, Stithians, Truro, Cornwall TR3 7DH
Tel: 01209 860003
Real Ales, Bar Food, Restaurant Menu,
No Smoking Area

137 Silver Ball
Fair Street, St Columb, Cornwall TR9 6LL
Tel: 01637 880632
Real Ales, Bar Food, Restaurant Menu,
Accommodation, No Smoking Area, Disabled Facilities

138 Skinners Ale House
58 East Street, Newquay, Cornwall TR7 1BE
Tel: 01637 876391
Real Ales, Bar Food, Restaurant Menu

139 Smugglers Den Inn
Trebellan, Cubert, Newquay, Cornwall TR8 5PY
Tel: 01637 830209
Real Ales, Bar Food, Restaurant Menu,
No Smoking Area

140 Sportsman Arms
Pencoys, Four Lanes, Redruth, Cornwall TR16 6LR
Tel: 01209 313724
Real Ales, Bar Food, Restaurant Menu,
No Smoking Area, Disabled Facilities

141 St Agnes Hotel
Church Street, Churchtown, St Agnes,
Cornwall TR5 0QP
Tel: 01872 552307
Real Ales, Bar Food, Restaurant Menu,
Accommodation, No Smoking Area

142 St Brannocks Hotel
Narrowcliff, Newquay, Cornwall TR7 2PN
Tel: 01637 872038
Bar Food, Restaurant Menu, Accommodation,
No Smoking Area, Disabled Facilities

143 St Day Inn
Fore Street, St Day, Redruth, Cornwall TR16 5JU
Tel: 01209 820573
Real Ales, Bar Food, Restaurant Menu,
Disabled Facilities
See panel below

143 St Day Inn
Fore Street, St Day, Cornwall TR16 5JU
☎ 01209 820573

Real Ales, Bar Food, Restaurant Menu,
Disabled Facilities

🖝   1 mile off the B3298 off the A30 (leave at Scorrier)

🍺   Bass

🍴   Bar meals 5-8, Sat 12-8, Sun L 12-3

🎵   Sun quiz, Thurs live music, Sat disco or karaoke

🅿   On street parking, beer garden

🕐   5-10.30, Sat & Sun from 12

🏛   Heritage Trail round St Day and neighbouring villages; Redruth 2 miles, Cambourne 5 miles

Sue and Garry are the genial hosts at the St Day Inn, a friendly pub that caters for the whole family. Sue produces very enjoyable bar meals every evening, all day on Saturday and a traditional roast Sunday lunch. The bar is in keeping with the inn's 18th century origins, with beams, brasses and a collection of model soldiers. A sheltered courtyard garden looks across rooftops to the village church tower.

144 St Pirans Inn
Holywell Bay, Newquay, Cornwall TR8 5PP
Tel: 01637 830205
Real Ales, Bar Food, Restaurant Menu,
No Smoking Area, Disabled Facilities

145 Stag Hunt Inn
20 St Michaels Rd, Ponsanooth, Falmouth,
Cornwall TR3 7EE
Tel: 01872 863046
Real Ales, Bar Food, Restaurant Menu,
Accommodation, No Smoking Area, Disabled Facilities

149 The Tavern

Mellanvrane Lane, Treninnick, nr Newquay,
Cornwall TR7 2LQ

☎ 01637 873564   🌐 www.taverninn.co.uk

**Real Ales, Bar Food, No Smoking Area,
Disabled Facilities**

☞ From the A30 take the road to Newquay; the
inn is on the outskirts of Newquay

🍺 Skinners Betty Stoggs, St Austell Tribute

🍴 Bar snacks 12-2, Sun L 12-2, Curry night Wed,
Steak night Sat

🎵 Live music Fri + 2 Sats a month, Jazz every
other Sun 1.30-4, Quiz Sun eve

⛰ Garden, car park

💳 Major cards except Amex and Diners

🕐 11-11 (Sun 12-10.30)

🏛 Newquay 1 mile

Steve, Karen and their hardworking staff welcome all comers to the Tavern, which stands amid glorious countryside yet just a short walk from the bustle of Newquay. Dating

back to the 18th century, it was built as a farmhouse, and the premises have been an inn for the past 40 years. Equally popular with locals and visitors from near and far, the inn has a lively, welcoming atmosphere, and the promise of the flower-festooned exterior is amply fulfilled within.

The main bar, family room and games room are full of charm, with plenty of cosy nooks and corners, and comfortable sofas

complement the usual tables and chairs. When the weather is kind, the courtyard garden comes into its own, and the weekend barbecues are always well attended. Bar snacks and meals are served from 12 to 2 Monday to Friday, ranging from baguettes, doorstop sandwiches and jacket potatoes to all-time favourites like Cornish pasties, sausage and mash, cottage pie and steaks. Booking is recommended for the Sunday roasts and for the special food nights – Wednesday is curry and a pint night, Saturday is steak night, with rump steak, gammon steak and chicken with all the trimmings. The attractions of this terrific inn extend to entertainment, with live music on Friday night and twice a month on Saturday, jazz every Sunday afternoon and a popular quiz (don't be late!) starting at 9 o'clock on Sunday evening.

Newquay is just down the road, with a whole host of attractions for all the family, but everyone visiting this busy resort should take time to visit the Tavern, firmly established as one of the very finest pubs in the whole county.

146 The Star Inn

Vogue , St Day, Redruth, Cornwall TR16 5NP
Tel: 01209 820242

Real Ales, Bar Food, Restaurant Menu,
No Smoking Area, Disabled Facilities

147 Surfside Hotel

12 Esplanade Rd, Pentire, Newquay,
Cornwall TR7 1QA
Tel: 01637 874432

Bar Food, Accommodation

148 The Swan

40 Bosvigo Road, Truro, Cornwall TR1 3DQ
Tel: 01872 225556

Real Ales, Disabled Facilities

149 Tavern

Treninnick, Newquay, Cornwall TR7 2LQ
Tel: 01637 873564

Real Ales, Bar Food, No Smoking Area,
Disabled Facilities

See panel opposite

150 Tocarne Hotel

Narrowcliff, Newquay, Cornwall TR7 2PW
Tel: 01637 872176

Real Ales, Restaurant Menu, Accommodation,
Disabled Facilities

151 Trefusis Arms

Clinton Rd, Redruth, Cornwall TR15 2LT
Tel: 01209 211813

Real Ales

152 Treguth Inn

Holywell Bay, Newquay, Cornwall TR8 5PP
Tel: 01637 830248

Real Ales, Bar Food, Restaurant Menu,
No Smoking Area

See panel on page 40

153 The Treleigh Arms

Treleigh, nr Redruth, Cornwall TR16 4AY
Tel: 01209 315095

Real Ales, Bar Food, Restaurant Menu, No Smoking
Area, Disabled Facilities

See panel below

153 The Treleigh Arms

Treleigh, nr Redruth, Cornwall TR16 4AY
☎ 01209 315095

Real Ales, Bar Food, Restaurant Menu,
No Smoking Area, Disabled Facilities

- On the A3047 between Scorrier and the A30
- Bass, locally brewed Mutiny, Knocker, Doom Bar, Dreckly
- 12-2 & 6.30-9
- Garden, car park
- Major cards accepted
- 11-3 & 6-11
- Redruth 1 mile, Portreath 4 miles, Truro 6 miles

In the tiny village of Treleigh, on the A3047 between Scorrier and the main A30, the Treleigh Arms provides a popular meeting place for local residents and a pleasant, civilised spot for motorists and tourists visiting the region. Décor and furnishings combine traditional and contemporary elements in the smart public rooms, while the newly completed beer garden, with water features and patio heaters, offers an alfresco alternative at any time of the year. Five real ales include locally brewed beers, and the eating options, ranging from hot and cold lunchtime snacks to the daily changing blackboard menu, are all home made . The Treleigh Arms is owned by Judith and Clive Welch, who have been together in the licensed trade for 30 years.

152 Treguth Inn

Holywell Bay, nr Newquay, Cornwall TR8 5PP
☎ 01637 830248

Real Ales, Bar Food, Restaurant Menu,
No Smoking Area

- ☞ The inn lies 3½ miles SW of Newquay off the A3075
- 🍺 Doom Bar + guests
- 🍴 L & D
- ♫ Quiz Wednesday
- ⛱ Gardens, car park
- 💳 Major cards accepted
- ⏱ L & D (all day in summer)
- 🏛 South West Coast Path; Newquay 3½ miles, Perranporth 4 miles

The **Treguth Inn** is a delightful example of a traditional Cornish inn, with a thatched roof, lovely gardens and a wealth of real old world character. Paul and Tresilla make

everyone welcome and keep them happy with excellent home cooking.

154 Tricky Dickie's

Tolgus Mount, Redruth, Cornwall TR15 3TA
Tel: 01209 219292

Real Ales, Bar Food, Restaurant Menu,
Accommodation, No Smoking Area, Disabled Facilities

155 Tuckingmill Hotel

Pendarves Street, Camborne, Cornwall TR14 8NJ
Tel: 01209 712165

Real Ales, Bar Food, Restaurant Menu,
No Smoking Area, Disabled Facilities

156 Two Clomes

East Road, Quintrell Downs, Newquay,
Cornwall TR8 4PD
Tel: 01637 871163

Real Ales, Bar Food, Restaurant Menu,
No Smoking Area

157 Tyacks Hotel

27 Commercial Street, Camborne,
Cornwall TR14 8LD
Tel: 01209 612424

Real Ales, Bar Food, Restaurant Menu,
Accommodation, No Smoking Area, Disabled Facilities

158 Tywarnhayle Hotel

The Square, Perranporth, Cornwall TR6 0ER
Tel: 01872 572215

Real Ales, Bar Food, Restaurant Menu,
No Smoking Area

159 Unicorn

Beach Road, Porthtowan, Cornwall TR4 8AD
Tel: 01209 890244

Real Ales, Bar Food, Restaurant Menu,
No Smoking Area, Disabled Facilities

160 Upper Deck

3 Boscawen Rd, Perranporth, Cornwall TR6 0EW
Tel: 01872 573865

Real Ales

161 Victoria Bars

5-6 King Street, Newquay, Cornwall TR7 1NB
Tel: 01637 872671

Real Ales, Disabled Facilities

162 The Victoria Inn

The Square, Four Lanes, Redruth,
Cornwall TR16 6PZ
Tel: 01209 216416

Real Ales, Bar Food, Restaurant Menu,
No Smoking Area, Disabled Facilities

163 The Victoria Inn

Chyvelah Road, Threemilestone, Truro,
Cornwall TR3 6BY
Tel: 01872 278313

Real Ales, Bar Food, Restaurant Menu,
Accommodation, No Smoking Area

164 Victory Inn

Towan Cross, Mount Hawke, Truro,
Cornwall TR4 8BZ
Tel: 01209 890359

Real Ales, Bar Food, Restaurant Menu,
No Smoking Area, Disabled Facilities

165 The Vyvyan Arms
Trelowarren Street, Camborne,
Cornwall TR14 8AN
Tel: 01209 712460

Real Ales

166 The Waggoners Arms
41 Trelowarren St, Camborne, Cornwall TR14 8AQ
Tel: 01209 718605

Real Ales, Disabled Facilities

167 Walkabout Inn
The Cresent, Newquay, Cornwall TR7 1DS
Tel: 01637 853000

Bar Food, Restaurant Menu, No Smoking Area,
Disabled Facilities

168 Waterfront Inn
Forth An Nance, Portreath, Redruth,
Cornwall TR16 4NQ
Tel: 01209 842777

Real Ales, Bar Food, Restaurant Menu,
No Smoking Area, Disabled Facilities

169 The Watering Hole
19 St Pirans Road, Perranporth, Cornwall TR6 0BH
Tel: 01872 572888

Real Ales, Bar Food, Restaurant Menu,
Disabled Facilities

See panel adjacent

170 The Wheel Inn
Tresillian, Truro, Cornwall TR2 4BA
Tel: 01872 520293

Real Ales, Bar Food, Restaurant Menu,
No Smoking Area

171 White Hart
Commerical St, Camborne, Cornwall TR14 8JZ
Tel: 01209 713102

Real Ales, Bar Food, Restaurant Menu,
No Smoking Area, Disabled Facilities

172 The White House Inn
Perranzabuloe, Truro, Cornwall TR4 9LQ
Tel: 01872 573306

Real Ales, Bar Food, Restaurant Menu,
No Smoking Area, Disabled Facilities

169 The Watering Hole
Perranporth Beach, Perranporth,
Cornwall TR6 0BH
☎ 01872 572888
⊕ www.the-wateringhole.co.uk

Real Ales, Bar Food, Restaurant Menu,
Disabled Facilities

☛ On the beach at Perranporth, 3 miles N of St
Agnes on the B3285

🍺 Skinners & St Austell brews

▮ 9am – 9.30pm

⚓ Beach, town car parks

💳 Major cards except Amex and Diners

🕐 All day Feb-Nov, Fri to Sun Dec and Jan

🏛 St Agnes 3 miles, Newquay 7 miles, Truro 10
miles

Starting life many years ago as a beach
shack, the Watering Hole has expanded
and evolved into a splendid drinking and
eating place in an unbeatable location right on
the beach. Three real ales are always available
at this busy, convivial spot, and food is served
during the long opening hours throughout the
premises or outside at picnic benches on the
beach.

173 Wig and Pen Inn and The Dock Restaurant
1 Frances Street, Truro, Cornwall TR1 3DP
Tel: 01872 273028

Real Ales, Bar Food, Restaurant Menu,
No Smoking Area, Disabled Facilities

174 William IVth
Kenwyn Street, Truro, Cornwall TR1 7DJ
Tel: 01872 273334

Real Ales, Bar Food, Restaurant Menu,
No Smoking Area, Disabled Facilities

175 The Willows
Kestle Mill, Newquay, Cornwall TR8 4PU
Tel: 01637 872286

Real Ales, Bar Food, Restaurant Menu,
No Smoking Area

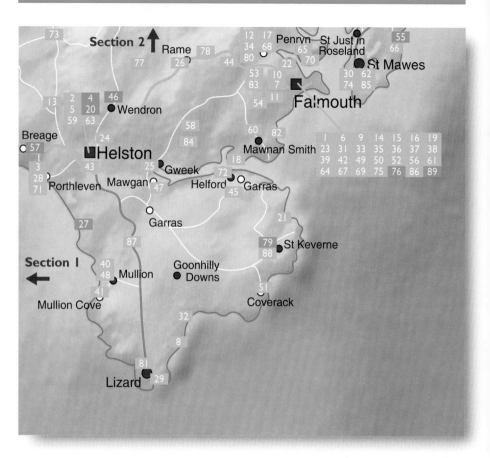

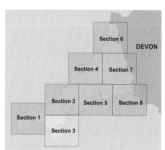

11	Pub or Inn Reference Number - Detailed Information
12	Pub or Inn Reference Number - Summary Entry
● ■	Place of interest mentioned in the chapter introduction

HELFORD & THE LIZARD

Warmed by the Gulf Stream, The Lizard Peninsula is home to the county's most interesting and exotic gardens, while Helford on the Helford Estuary and St Mawes in the shelter of Carrick Roads, are favourite sailing centres. Helston is the home of the famous furry or Flora Dance, and the deep-water harbour of Falmouth is protected by Pendennis Castle, one of Henry VIII's great fortresses. Other magnets for visitors to this region include the National Seal Santuary at Gweek and the amazing Earth Satellite Station at Goonhilly Downs.

Falmouth

In Britain's Western Approaches, guarding the entrance into Carrick Roads, Falmouth is a spectacular deep-water anchorage that is the world's third deepest natural harbour. Henry VIII's **Pendennis Castle**, on a 200ft promontory, is one of Cornwall's great fortresses, and was one of the last Royalist strongholds to fall in the Civil War. Most of the town's attractions are linked to the sea, including the **National Maritime Museum Cornwall** on Discovery Quay. On Custom House Quay stands an early-19th century brick chimney and incinerator known as the **Queen's Pipe**. It was here that contraband tobacco seized by Falmouth customs men was burnt.

Goonhilly Downs

With its 60 dishes and the latest technology, the **Earth Satellite Station** handles simultaneously millions of international phone calls, e-mails and TV broadcasts. The guided tour round the site is a fascinating, rewarding and educational experience. The downland surrounding the station was purchased by the Nature Conservancy Council (now English heritage) as Cornwall's first nature reserve.

Gweek

A short distance from the centre of Gweek, on the picturesque reaches of the Helford Estuary, is the **National Seal Sanctuary**, Europe's leading marine animal rescue centre.

Helford

A picture-postcard village on the tree-lined south bank of the Helford Estuary. Once the haunt of smugglers, who took advantage of the many isolated creeks and inlets, it is now a popular sailing cantre.

Helford

43

Helston

Helston is the home of the celebrated **Furry** or **Flora Dance**, and the **Festival of the Furry**, an annual pageant of music and dance, always attracts large crowds. The **Guildhall** and the **Folk Museum** are among the town's many interesting buildings, and a short drive away are two very popular visitor attractions

The Lizard

– **Trevarno Estate** incorporating the **National Museum of Gardening**, and **Flambards Victorian Village** with its reconstruction of a lamplit Victorian street. Close to Flambards is the Royal Navy's land and sea rescue headquarters at **Culdrose**, one of the largest and busiest helicopter bases in Europe.

Lizard

The most southerly village in mainland Britain, Lizard is a place of craft shops, cafés, art galleries and a busy inn, all clustered round the green. To the south lies **Lizard Point**, the tip of the Lizard peninsula, with a twin-towered lighthouse.

Mawnan Smith

To the west of this pretty village overlooking the River Helford lies the National Trust's **Glendurgan**, a marvellous jungly valley garden with many unique features.

Mullion

The largest settlement on the Lizard peninsula, with a church dedicated to St

Mallenus (Malo). The church has some interesting carved bench ends and a 'dog door' that was used by sheepdogs, who were allowed to attend services with their masters but were made to leave if they misbehaved. Much of the land around **Mullion Cove**, as well as offshore **Mullion Island**, is in the care of the National Trust.

St Just in Roseland

The 13th parish church enjoys one of the most superb settings in the county, surrounded by gardens with sub-tropical trees and shrubs. A V Morton, in his book *In Search of England*, called the churchyard 'one of the little known glories of England'.

St Keverne

This pleasant village is fairly unusual for Cornwall in two ways. It has a village square, a rarity in the county, and its parish church is one of the few in Cornwall with a spire. From its elevated position on a high plateau the spire has long been used as a landmark for ships attempting to negotiate the dangerous rocks known as **The Manacles** that lie just offshore.

St Mawes

Long before it became a popular sailing and holiday centre, St Mawes was an important part of the region's coastal defences; the artillery fort **St Mawes Castle**, built around 1540 by Henry VIII, still dominates the place.

Wendron

Close to Wendron is one of the many mines worked in the area since the 15th century. The **Poldark Mine Heritage Centre** offers guided underground tours through the mine's extensive tunnels.

1 Anacapri Hotel

Gyllyngvase Rd, Falmouth, Cornwall TR11 4DJ
Tel: 01326 311454

Restaurant Menu, Accommodation, No Smoking Area, Disabled Facilities

2 Angel Hotel

16 Coinagehall St, Helston, Cornwall TR13 8EB
Tel: 01326 572701

Bar Food, Accommodation, No Smoking Area

3 Atlantic Inn

Peverell Terrace, Helston, Cornwall TR13 9DZ
Tel: 01326 562439

Real Ales, Bar Food, Restaurant Menu,
No Smoking Area, Disabled Facilities

4 The Bell Inn

Meneage Street, Helston, Cornwall TR13 8AA
Tel: 01326 572134

Real Ales, No Smoking Area, Disabled Facilities
See panel below

4 The Bell Inn

Meneage Street, Helston, Cornwall TR13 8AA
☎ 01326 572134

Real Ales, No Smoking Area, Disabled Facilities

☛ Close to the centre of Helston, 3 miles from Porthleven and the coast

🍺 Old Speckled Hen, Ring o 'Bells

🍴 Bring your own food

♫ Pool table, live music monthly

⛲ Garden

🕐 11-11 (to 12 Fri & Sat)

🏛 Porthleven 3 miles, Helford River 3 miles, Poldark Mines 3 miles

We've got the pub. You bring the grub' read the boards outside **The Bell Inn**, a convivial town-centre inn that's open all day, every day to welcome old friends and new.

The bars have a traditional appeal of stone walls, stone or wooden floors, open fires and plenty of comfortable seats. In one part of the bar Premier League football and other major sports events are shown on a big screen. As the boards suggest, customers can bring their own food here, and there's an excellent selection of ales (including the Bodmin-brewed Ring o'Bells) and bottled beers to accompany the 'grub'.

The Bell is a sponsor of the Helston Beer Festival held each year in the spring. This is very much a pub for all the family, and a new children's play area has been created in the walled garden.

5 Blue Anchor Inn

50 Coinagehall Street, Helston, Cornwall TR13 8EL
Tel: 01326 562821

Real Ales, Bar Food, Restaurant Menu,
Accommodation, No Smoking Area, Disabled Facilities

6 The Boathouse

Trevethan Hill, Falmouth, Cornwall TR11 2AG
Tel: 01326 315425

Real Ales, Bar Food, Restaurant Menu,
No Smoking Area, Disabled Facilities

7 Boslowick Inn

Prislow Lane, Falmouth, Cornwall TR11 4PZ
Tel: 01326 312010

Real Ales, Bar Food, Restaurant Menu,
No Smoking Area, Disabled Facilities

8 Cadgwith Cove Inn

Cadgwith Drive, Cadgwith, Helston,
Cornwall TR12 7JX
Tel: 01326 290513

Real Ales, Bar Food, Restaurant Menu,
Accommodation, No Smoking Area, Disabled Facilities

9 The Chain Locker

Quay Hill, Falmouth, Cornwall TR11 3HG
Tel: 01326 311085

Real Ales, Bar Food

10 The Clipper Way

Mongleath Road, Falmouth, Cornwall TR11 4PN
Tel: 01326 313831

Real Ales, Bar Food, Restaurant Menu,
No Smoking Area, Disabled Facilities

11 Crill Manor

Maen Valley, Budock Water, Falmouth,
Cornwall TR11 5BL
Tel: 01326 211880

Restaurant Menu, Accommodation, No Smoking Area

12 Cross Keys

7 Church Road, Penryn, Cornwall TR10 8DA
Tel: 01326 373233

Real Ales, Bar Food, Restaurant Menu,
No Smoking Area, Disabled Facilities

13 Crown Inn

Crowntown, Helston, Cornwall TR13 0AD
Tel: 01326 565538

Real Ales, Bar Food, Restaurant Menu,
Accommodation, No Smoking Area, Disabled Facilities

14 The Cutty Sark

4 Grove Place, Falmouth, Cornwall TR11 4AU
Tel: 01326 311859

Real Ales, Bar Food, Restaurant Menu,
No Smoking Area, Disabled Facilities

15 Falmouth Beach Resort Hotel

Gyllyngvase Beach, Seafront, Falmouth,
Cornwall TR11 4NA
Tel: 01326 312999

Real Ales, Bar Food, Restaurant Menu,
Accommodation, No Smoking Area, Disabled Facilities

16 Falmouth Hotel

Castle Beach, Cliff Road, Falmouth,
Cornwall TR11 4NZ
Tel: 01326 312671

Bar Food, Restaurant Menu, Accommodation,
No Smoking Area, Disabled Facilities

17 The Famous Barrel

St Thomas St, Penryn, Cornwall TR10 8JP
Tel: 01326 373505

Real Ales

18 Ferry Boat Inn

Helford Passage, Falmouth, Cornwall TR11 5LB
Tel: 01326 250625

Real Ales, Bar Food, Restaurant Menu,
Accommodation, No Smoking Area, Disabled Facilities

20 The Fitzsimmons Arms

Coinagehall Street, Helston, Cornwall TR13 8EQ
☎ 01326 574897

Real Ales, Bar Food, Restaurant Menu,
No Smoking Area, Disabled Facilities

☞ The inn is in the centre of Helston, 3 miles from Porthleven and the coast

🍺 Sharp's, Abbot Ale. Cornish guest ales and cider

🍴 Popular snacks and meals

♫ Live music Thurs, DJ Fri/Sat, karaoke Sun

⛲ Super beer garden

🕐 11-11

🏛 Flambards Theme Park 2 miles, Mawgan National Seal Sanctuary 3 miles, Helford Estuary 4 miles, Poldark Mines 3 miles, Mullion Cove 5 miles

Built in 1818 and originally called The Seven Stars, The Fitzsimmons Arms stands on the main street of a pleasant town three miles from the coast. Hanging baskets make a cheerful sight outside the pub, and at the back is a really superb beer garden created by proprietor David Slade. David and his staff offer traditional Cornish hospitality in an ambience that combines period appeal with 21st century comfort, and the bars are ideal spots for enjoying local cask ales and ciders and good home cooking. An upstairs panelled games room has a pool table and dart board. The name of the pub commemorates one of the town's most famous sons, the bare-knuckle boxer Bob Fitzsimmons, and photographs, prints and other boxing memorabilia are an eyecatching feature of the decor.

19 Finn Mccoul's

1 Killigrew Street, Falmouth, Cornwall TR11 3PG
Tel: 01326 318653

Real Ales, Bar Food

20 Fitzsimmons Arms

Coinagehall St, Helston, Cornwall TR13 8EQ
Tel: 01326 574897

Real Ales, Bar Food, Restaurant Menu,
No Smoking Area, Disabled Facilities

See panel above

21 Five Pilchards Inn

Porthallow, St Keverne, Cornwall TR12 6PP
Tel: 01326 280256

Real Ales, Bar Food, Restaurant Menu,
Disabled Facilities

22 Four Winds Inn

Dracaena Avenue, Falmouth, Cornwall TR11 2EW
Tel: 01326 311369

Real Ales, Bar Food, Restaurant Menu,
No Smoking Area, Disabled Facilities

23 Grapes Inn

64 Church St, Falmouth, Cornwall TR11 3DS
Tel: 01326 314704

Real Ales, Bar Food, Restaurant Menu,
No Smoking Area

24 Gwealdues Hotel

Falmouth Road, Helston, Cornwall TR13 8JX
Tel: 01326 572808

Real Ales, Bar Food, Restaurant Menu,
Accommodation, No Smoking Area, Disabled Facilities

25 Gweek Inn

Gweek, Helston, Cornwall TR12 6TU
Tel: 01326 221502

Bar Food, Restaurant Menu, No Smoking Area,
Disabled Facilities

26 Halfway House

Rame Cross Village, Penryn, Cornwall TR10 9ED
Tel: 01209 860222

Real Ales, Bar Food, Restaurant Menu,
Accommodation, Disabled Facilities

27 Halzephron Inn

Gunwalloe, Helston, Cornwall TR12 7QB
Tel: 01326 240406

Real Ales, Bar Food, Restaurant Menu,
Accommodation, No Smoking Area, Disabled Facilities

See panel below

28 The Harbour Inn

Commercial Rd, Porthleven, Helston,
Cornwall TR13 9JB
Tel: 01326 573876

Real Ales, Bar Food, Restaurant Menu,
Accommodation, No Smoking Area, Disabled Facilities

29 Housel Bay Hotel

Housel Cove, The Lizard, Cornwall TR12 7PG
Tel: 01326 290417

Bar Food, Restaurant Menu, Accommodation,
No Smoking Area, Disabled Facilities

30 Idle Rocks Hotel

1 Tredenham Road, St Mawes, Truro,
Cornwall TR2 5AN
Tel: 01326 270771

Restaurant Menu, Accommodation, No Smoking Area

27 The Halzephron Inn

Gunwalloe, nr Helston, Cornwall TR12 7QB

☎ 01326 240406   ⊕ www.eatoutcornwall.com

Real Ales, Bar Food, Restaurant Menu,
Accommodation, No Smoking Area, Disabled
Facilities

- ☛ Leave the A3083 Helston-Lizard road at Gunwalloe and follow signs to the inn
- 🍺 Halzephron Gold Original
- 🍴 12-2 & 7-9
- 🛏 2 rooms en suite
- 🪑 Terrace front and side
- 💳 Major cards except Diners
- 🏆 Good Pub Guide's Cornwall Dining Pub of the Year 2005
- 🕐 Lunchtime and evening
- 🏛 South Cornwall Footpath 300 yards, Church of St Winwalloe 1 mile, Helston 4 miles

Food is king at the **Halzephron Inn**, which stands on the Cornish cliffs just 300 yards from the South Cornwall footpath. Proprietor Angela Thomas, a lifelong Cornwall resident, has been involved in the business for more than 20 years, and in making this one of the best eating places in the whole county is carrying on in the tradition of her late husband Harry. Superb seafood dishes are just one of the highlights on the menu, and there's also a great choice for meat-eaters and vegetarians. The inn has long been a much-loved 'local', serving great beers from local breweries (try Halzephron Gold from a micro-brewery) and entertaining with darts, dominoes and cribbage. And the two en suite double bedrooms make this a perfect place for a holiday.

31 Jacobs Ladder Inn

Chapel Terrace, Falmouth, Cornwall TR11 3BQ
Tel: 01326 311010

Bar Food, Accommodation, No Smoking Area,
Disabled Facilities

32 The Kennack Sands Inn

Kuggar, Ruan Minor, Helston, Cornwall TR12 7LT
Tel: 01326 290547

Real Ales, Bar Food, Restaurant Menu,
Accommodation, No Smoking Area, Disabled Facilities

33 Killigrew Inn

95-97 Killigrew Street, Falmouth,
Cornwall TR11 3PU
Tel: 01326 311180

Real Ales

34 Kings Arms Public House

3 Broad Street, Penryn, Cornwall TR10 8JL
Tel: 01326 372336

Real Ales, Bar Food, No Smoking Area,
Disabled Facilities

35 The Kings Head

32 Church Street, Falmouth, Cornwall TR11 3EQ
Tel: 01326 319469

Bar Food, Restaurant Menu, No Smoking Area,
Disabled Facilities

36 Maderia Hotel

Cliff Road, Falmouth, Cornwall TR11 4NY
Tel: 01326 313531

Bar Food, Restaurant Menu, Accommodation,
No Smoking Area, Disabled Facilities

37 Maenheere Hotel

Grove Place, Falmouth, Cornwall TR11 4AL
Tel: 01326 312009

Accommodation

38 Masons Arms

31 Killigrew Street, Falmouth, Cornwall TR11 3PW
Tel: 01326 311061

Real Ales

39 The Mi Bar

6-7 Church St, Falmouth, Cornwall TR11 3DP
Tel: 01326 316909

Bar Food, Restaurant Menu

40 Mounts Bay Inn

Churchtown, Mullion , Helston,
Cornwall TR12 7HN
Tel: 01326 240221

Real Ales, Bar Food, Restaurant Menu,
Accommodation, No Smoking Area, Disabled Facilities

41 Mullion Cove Hotel

Mullion, Helston, Cornwall TR12 7EP
Tel: 01326 240328

Bar Food, Restaurant Menu, Accommodation,
No Smoking Area, Disabled Facilities

42 Nancys

4 Killigrew Street, Falmouth, Cornwall TR11 3PN
Tel: 01326 319100

Real Ales, Disabled Facilities

43 Nansloe Manor Hotel and Restaurant

Meneage Road, Helston, Cornwall TR13 0SB
Tel: 01326 574691

Real Ales, Restaurant Menu, Accommodation,
No Smoking Area, Disabled Facilities

44 New Inn

Church Rd, Mabe Burnthouse, Penryn,
Cornwall TR10 9HN
Tel: 01326 373428

Real Ales, Bar Food, Restaurant Menu,
No Smoking Area, Disabled Facilities

45 New Inn

Manaccan, Helston, Cornwall TR12 6HA
Tel: 01326 231323

Real Ales, Bar Food, Restaurant Menu,
No Smoking Area, Disabled Facilities

46 New Inn

Wendron, Helston, Cornwall TR13 0EA
Tel: 01326 572683

Real Ales, Bar Food, Restaurant Menu,
No Smoking Area, Disabled Facilities

See panel below

47 Old Court House Inn

Mawgan, Helston, Cornwall TR12 6AD
Tel: 01326 221240

Real Ales, Bar Food, No Smoking Area

48 Old Inn

Churchtown, Mullion, Helston,
Cornwall TR12 7HN
Tel: 01326 240240

Real Ales, Bar Food, Restaurant Menu,
No Smoking Area, Disabled Facilities

49 The Packet Station

4 The Moor, Falmouth, Cornwall TR11 3QA
Tel: 01326 310110

Real Ales, Bar Food, No Smoking Area,
Disabled Facilities

50 Palm Court Hotel (Falmouth) Ltd

Melvill Rd, Falmouth, Cornwall TR11 4BE
Tel: 01326 313076

Bar Food, Restaurant Menu, Accommodation,
No Smoking Area

51 Paris Hotel

The Coverdales, Coverack, Helston,
Cornwall TR12 6SX
Tel: 01326 280258

Real Ales, Bar Food, Restaurant Menu,
Accommodation, No Smoking Area, Disabled Facilities

---

46 The New Inn

Wendron, nr Helston, Cornwall TR13 0EA
☎ 01326 572683

**Real Ales, Bar Food, Restaurant Menu,
No Smoking Area, Disabled Facilities**

- ☞ The inn lies on the B3297 2 miles north of Helston
- 🍺 Skinner's, St Austell, guest ales in summer
- 🍴 Full menu including speciality steaks
- ⚓ Beer garden
- 💳 Major cards
- 🕐 12-3 & 6-11 (all day in summer)
- 🏛 Helston 2 miles, Flambards 2 miles, Poldark Mines 1 mile, Trevarno Gardens 6 miles, Porthleven 4 miles

Easy to find on the B3297 north of Helston, The New Inn has a welcome for 'one and all' – as it says on the pub sign. Behind the facade of this fine old stone inn, with its cheerful red awning and flowers and shrubs in pots and window boxes, the inside is equally appealing, and the bar is a very pleasant spot for enjoying a glass of the excellent Cornish brews available. Nigel and Angie, who came here in the spring of 2005 after running a hotel in Falmouth, have converted the lounge bar into a comfortable, atmospheric non-smoking restaurant. The wide-ranging menu features much local produce, including fish and shellfish landed at Porthleven, sizzling sirloin steaks, Sunday roasts and great puds. In the summer, when the pub is open all day, traditional cream teas are a popular treat.

52 Penmere Manor

Mongleath Road, Falmouth, Cornwall TR11 4PN
Tel: 01326 211411

Real Ales, Bar Food, Restaurant Menu,
Accommodation, No Smoking Area, Disabled Facilities

53 Penmorvah Manor Hotel

Budock Water, Falmouth, Cornwall TR11 5ED
Tel: 01326 250277

Real Ales, Bar Food, Restaurant Menu,
Accommodation, No Smoking Area, Disabled Facilities

54 Pirate Inn

7 Grove Place, Falmouth, Cornwall TR11 4AU
Tel: 01326 311288

Real Ales, Bar Food, Restaurant Menu,
No Smoking Area, Disabled Facilities

55 Plume Of Feathers

The Square, Portscatho, Truro, Cornwall TR2 5HW
Tel: 01872 580321

Real Ales, Bar Food, No Smoking Area,
Disabled Facilities

See panel below

56 Quayside Inn and The Old Ale House

11 Arwenack Street, Falmouth, Cornwall TR11 3JQ
Tel: 01326 312113

Real Ales, Bar Food, Restaurant Menu,
No Smoking Area, Disabled Facilities

57 Queens Arms

Breage, Helston, Cornwall TR13 9PD
Tel: 01326 573485

Real Ales, Bar Food, Restaurant Menu,
No Smoking Area, Disabled Facilities

See panel on page 52

55 The Plume of Feathers

Portscatho, nr St Mawes, Cornwall TR2 5HW
☎ 01782 580321

Real Ales, Bar Food, No Smoking Area,
Disabled Facilities

- 14 miles south of Truro off the A3078
- St Austell Brewery ales
- Lunch and dinner menus + daily specials
- Not Amex
- Cask Marque
- 11-2.30 & 6.30-11 (all day in summer)
- South West Coast Path; St Mawes 5 miles, Trelissick Garden 6 miles, Truro 14 miles

Fishermen's cottages dating back 500 years, with stone walls outside and in, have been converted into a delightful inn a short walk from the beach and car park.

Host Graham Thomas has been here for more than 30 years and has made the inn a great favourite with both the residents of Portscatho and the tourists who throng the area in summer.

Cask Marque ales include several of the St Austell brews, and in the two non-smoking dining areas the dishes served are generously served and very tasty.

Typical choices (the menu changes regularly) might include tomato & courgette soup, Thai chilli chicken stir-fry, red pepper and sweet pepper tartlets, and hot chocolate fudge cake.

57 The Queens Arms

Breage, nr Helston, Cornwall TR13 9PD
☎ 01326 573485

Real Ales, Bar Food, Restaurant Menu,
No Smoking Area, Disabled Facilities

- In the village of Breage, 3 miles W of Helston
- Sharps
- Lunchtime and evening
- Jazz Thursday
- Car park
- ATM on site.
- Lunchtime and evening
- Praa Sands 2 miles, Helston 3 miles

Hardworking Alec Robertson, a recently elected county councillor, owns one of the most popular pubs in this part of South Cornwall.

On the A394 between Penzance and the Lizard Peninsula, the **Queens Arms** has a bar with open fires at both ends, a splendid place to relax and enjoy good conversation and a glass of one of the six real ales that are always available. There's also a good wine list to compliment the food served in the bar or non-smoking restaurant. Steaks, sausages and pizzas are among the favourite orders.

With its fantastic atmosphere and great food, the Queens Arms has become almost as well known to visitors to Breage as the Church of St Breaca with its superb wall paintings that stands opposite.

58 Queen's Arms Inn
Fore Street, Constantine, Falmouth,
Cornwall TR11 5AB
Tel: 01326 340254
Real Ales, Bar Food, No Smoking Area,
Disabled Facilities

59 The Red Lion
Church Street, Helston, Cornwall TR13 8TG
Tel: 01326 572293
Real Ales, Bar Food, No Smoking Area,
Disabled Facilities

60 Red Lion Inn
Mawnan Smith, Falmouth, Cornwall TR11 5EP
Tel: 01326 250026
Real Ales, Bar Food, Restaurant Menu,
No Smoking Area, Disabled Facilities

61 Remedies Bar
The Moor, Falmouth, Cornwall TR11 3QA
Tel: 01326 314454
Disabled Facilities

62 Rising Sun Hotel
The Square, St Mawes, Truro, Cornwall TR2 5DJ
Tel: 01326 270233
Real Ales, Bar Food, Restaurant Menu,
Accommodation, No Smoking Area, Disabled Facilities

63 Rodney Inn
31 Meneage Street, Helston, Cornwall TR13 8AA
Tel: 01326 572417
Real Ales, Bar Food, Restaurant Menu,
No Smoking Area, Disabled Facilities

64 Royal Duchy Hotel
Cliff Road, Falmouth, Cornwall TR11 4NX
Tel: 01326 313042
Real Ales, Bar Food, Restaurant Menu,
Accommodation, No Smoking Area, Disabled Facilities

65 Royal Standard
St Peters Hill, Flushing, Falmouth,
Cornwall TR11 5TP
Tel: 01326 374250
Real Ales, Bar Food

66 Royal Standard Inn
The Square, Gerrans, Truro, Cornwall TR2 5EB
Tel: 01872 580271

Real Ales, Bar Food, Restaurant Menu,
No Smoking Area, Disabled Facilities

67 Seaview Inn
Wodehouse Terrace, Falmouth, Cornwall TR11 3EP
Tel: 01326 311359

Real Ales, Bar Food, Accommodation

68 The Seven Stars
The Terrace, Penryn, Cornwall TR10 8EH
Tel: 01326 373573

Real Ales

69 Seven Stars
1 The Moor , Falmouth, Cornwall TR11 3QA
Tel: 01326 312111

Real Ales

70 Seven Stars Inn
Trefusis Road, Flushing, Falmouth,
Cornwall TR11 5TY
Tel: 01326 374373

Real Ales, Bar Food, Restaurant Menu,
Accommodation, No Smoking Area, Disabled Facilities

71 Ship Inn
Porthleven, Cornwall TR13 9JS
Tel: 01326 564204

Real Ales, Bar Food, Restaurant Menu,
No Smoking Area

72 Shipwrights Arms
Helford, Helston, Cornwall TR12 6JX
Tel: 01326 231235

Real Ales, Bar Food, Restaurant Menu,
No Smoking Area, Disabled Facilities

73 St Aubyns Arms
The Square , Praze, Camborne, Cornwall TR14 0JR
Tel: 01209 831425

Real Ales, Bar Food, Restaurant Menu,
No Smoking Area, Disabled Facilities

74 St Mawes Hotel
Sea Front, St Mawes, Cornwall TR2 5DW
Tel: 01326 270266

Real Ales, Bar Food, Restaurant Menu,
Accommodation, No Smoking Area, Disabled Facilities

75 St Micheal's Hotel & Spa
Gyllyngvase Beach, Seafront, Falmouth,
Cornwall TR11 4NB
Tel: 01326 312707

Bar Food, Restaurant Menu, Accommodation,
No Smoking Area, Disabled Facilities

76 Star and Garter
52 High Street, Falmouth, Cornwall TR11 2AF
Tel: 01326 318313

Real Ales, Bar Food
See panel below

76 The Star & Garter
52 High Street, Falmouth, Cornwall TR11 2AF
☎ 01326 318313

Real Ales, Bar Food

☛ On the high street coming into Falmouth, 8 miles S of Truro on the A39

🍺 Two ales from local breweries

🍴 12-2, also 6-9 Thurs-Sat

🎵 Rock & Blues weekends, jazz Monday, Guitar soloist Thursday

💳 Major cards except Amex

🕐 11-11 (Sun 12-10.30)

🏛 All the attractions of Falmouth; Mawnan Smith 3 miles, Glendurgan NT 4 miles, Truro 8 miles

On the High Street coming into Falmouth, overlooking the Harbour, The Star & Garter has a cheerful relaxed atmosphere generated by long-time tenants Jane Collins and Paul Dash. In the stylishly modernised public areas the choice of real ales changes regularly, and the menu features super seafood dishes, including the renowned crab cakes. The pub is the HQ of the Falmouth Marine Band, which raises money for charity.

79 The Three Tuns

The Square, St Keverne, The Lizard,
Cornwall TR12 6NA
☎ 01326 280949
🌐 www.thethreetunsstkeverne.co.uk

**Real Ales, Bar Food, Restaurant Menu,
Accommodation, No Smoking Area**

🖝 St Keverne lies at the end of the B3293 9
miles southeast of Helston

🍺 Sharp's and Cornish guests beer

🍴 Popular dishes including seafood specials

🛏 6 guest rooms

🎵 Boat trips, weekly quiz, monthly live music

🍻 Garden, playground, car park

💳 Major cards

🕐 12-3 & 6-11 (all day Sat & Sun)

🏛 Parish church; coast path; Helston 9 miles

A village square is quite an unusual feature in Cornwall, and on the square at St Keverne stands a delightful old stone pub with many attractive features. The interior is warm and traditional, with high ceilings and lots of period photographs, creating just the right ambience for enjoying good Cornish ales and unpretentious home cooking including locally landed fish and shellfish. Tables are set out on a covered terrace, beyond which is a garden with a safe children's play area and views towards Falmouth Bay. St Keverne is an ideal base for exploring the Lizard peninsula, and the Three Tuns has three comfortable, recently refurbished en suite guest bedrooms, and three which are not en suite. Also on the square is the parish church, whose spire (another rarity in Cornwall) has long been a landmark for sailors in the dangerous coastal waters.

77 The Star Inn

Porkellis, Helston, Cornwall TR13 0JR
Tel: 01326 340237

Real Ales, Bar Food

78 The Stonemasons Arms

Longdowns, Penryn, Cornwall TR10 9DL
Tel: 01209 860724

Real Ales, Bar Food, No Smoking Area,
Disabled Facilities

79 Three Tuns

The Square, St Keverne, Cornwall TR12 6NA
Tel: 01326 280949

Real Ales, Bar Food, Restaurant Menu,
Accommodation, No Smoking Area

See panel above

80 Three Tuns Inn

18 West Street , Penryn, Cornwall TR10 8EW
Tel: 01326 373977

Real Ales, Bar Food, Restaurant Menu,
No Smoking Area, Disabled Facilities

81 The Top House

The Lizard, Helston, Cornwall TR12 7NQ
Tel: 01326 290974

Bar Food, Restaurant Menu, No Smoking Area,
Disabled Facilities

82 Trelawne Hotel

Maenporth Road, Falmouth, Cornwall TR11 5HS
Tel: 01326 250417

Bar Food, Accommodation, No Smoking Area

83 Trelowarren Arms

Budock Water, Falmouth, Cornwall TR11 5DR
Tel: 01326 372264

Real Ales, Bar Food, Restaurant Menu,
No Smoking Area, Disabled Facilities

84 Trengilly Wartha Inn

Nancenoy, Constantine, Falmouth,
Cornwall TR11 5RP
Tel: 01326 340332

Real Ales, Bar Food, Restaurant Menu,
Accommodation, No Smoking Area, Disabled Facilities

85 Victory Inn

Victory Steps, St Mawes, Truro, Cornwall TR2 5DQ
Tel: 01326 270324

Real Ales, Bar Food, Restaurant Menu,
Accommodation, No Smoking Area

86 The Water Front Bar

Custom House Quay, Falmouth, Cornwall TR11 3JT
Tel: 01326 212168

Real Ales

87 Wheel Inn

Cross Lanes, Helston, Cornwall TR12 7AY
Tel: 01326 240412

Real Ales, Bar Food, Restaurant Menu,
No Smoking Area, Disabled Facilities

88 White Hart

The Square, St Keverne, Helston,
Cornwall TR12 6ND
Tel: 01326 280325

Real Ales, Bar Food, Restaurant Menu,
No Smoking Area, Disabled Facilities

89 Wodehouse Arms

Killigrew Street, Falmouth, Cornwall TR11 3PN
Tel: 01326 312534

Real Ales, Bar Food

See panel below

89 The Wodehouse Arms

16 Killigrew Street, Falmouth, Cornwall TR11 3PN
☎ 01326 312534

Real Ales, Bar Food

☞ Opposite the main Post Office back from the
riverfront in the centre of Falmouth

🍺 St Austell Tinners and Tribute

🍴 11-3 & 5.30-8 (Sun 12-4)

🎵 Pool, darts, Sky Sports, entertainment
Thursday & Saturday

💷 Cash only

🕐 11-11

🏛 All the attractions of Falmouth

In the heart of Falmouth, opposite the main
Post Office and a short stroll from the river,
the **Wodehouse Arms** dates back to the 18th
century. It's the first venture into the licensed
trade for Andrew and Caroline Gray, who took
over as tenants in March 2005. Caroline is a
first-class cook and her tempting menu based
on locally sourced produce includes popular
classics such as ham & eggs, steaks and mixed
grills. A lighter menu is available from opening
time to early evening. Tribute and Tinners from
the St Austell Brewery head the list of ales, and
the well-stocked bar also offers a good
selection of other draught and bottled beers,
lagers, wines, spirits and soft drinks. Pool and
darts are played at one end of the bar, and
major sports events are shown on a 6ft TV
screen.

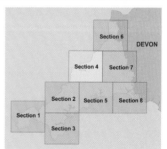

	Pub or Inn Reference Number - Detailed Information
11	
12	Pub or Inn Reference Number - Summary Entry
●■	Place of interest mentioned in the chapter introduction

PADSTOW & WADEBRIDGE AREA

The King Arthur connection brings visitors from all over the world to Cornwall and those connections are strongest in Tintagel. In this area also are the busy towns of Wadebridge and Padstow, the varied delights of Bodmin and the tranquil church of St Enedoc where the grave of Sir John Betjeman is a place of pilgrimage for many.

Boscastle

This delightful little port hit the headlines in August 2004, when a 12ft wave of mud and water swept down the valley of the River Valency and destroyed many historic and picturesque buildings. One of the most interesting was the unique **Museum of Witchcraft** down by the harbour.

Bodmin

Midway between Cornwall's north and south coasts, Bodmin has plenty to attract the visitor. Among the best-known places of interest are **Bodmin Jail**, the **Shire Hall** with its **Courtroom Experience**, **Bodmin Town Museum** and the **Duke of Cornwall's Light Infantry Regimental Museum**. Here too are the headquarters of the steam-hauled **Bodmin & Wenford Railway**.

Camelford

On the northern fringe of Bodmin Moor, Camelford is one of several places that lay claim to being the site of King Arthur's Camelot, and the **Arthurian Centre** at Slaughterbridge tells his story. Other attractions include the **North Cornwall Museum and Gallery**, the **British Cycling Museum** and the nearby **Gaia Energy Centre**, which promotes renewable energy and conservation through exhibits and educational programmes. It stands on the site of Britain's first commercial wind farm.

Bodmin Moor

Cutmadoc

Two miles south of Bodmin, Cutmadoc is the closest village to the spectacular estate of **Lanhydrock House**, one of the National Trust's most visited properties. It is possibly the most complete grand Victorian house in Britain, and the gardens and grounds are also a pure delight.

Delabole

Slate was and is king at this village, which is almost literally built of slate. The huge crater of **Delabole Slate Quarry**, where slate is still mined, is half a mile wide and 500 feet deep, and provides a unique opportunity for walkabout tours where visitors can watch all the processes as they happen.

Padstow

Throughout the summer months the harbour and shopping streets of Padstow throng with visitors. The old quarter has managed to retain much of its medieval character, and the influence of the sea is never far away: two notable examples are

Rick Stein's famous seafood restaurant and the **National Lobster Hatchery** on South Quay.

Polzeath

Holidaymakers and surfers flock to the small resorts of Polzetah and New Polzeath, and the fine sands, the caves and the tidal rock pools are guaranteed to keep the children happy.

Port Isaac

A wonderful old-world fishing village that has kept much of its ancient charm and character. The centre of this conservation village is centred round the harbour, and the narrow streets and lanes and alleys are wonderful places to explore.

St Mawgan

The restored **Church of St Mawgan and St Nicholas** boasts one of the finest collections of monumental brasses in the country, many of them relating to the influential Arundell family. In the churchyard is a beautifully carved lantern cross dating from around 1420.

Tintagel

The close connections with King Arthur bring visitors from all over the world to the small coastal village of Tintagel. The Castle, whose romantic ruins stand on a wild and windswept headland, is said to be the birthplace of the King,

Padstow

Tintagel Castle

stretch of coast, but what draws most visitors to this tranquil place is the black slate headstone that marks the grave of Sir John Betjeman. He spent many childhood holidays in the area, and he recalled those days in one of his best-known poems, called simply *Trebetherick*.

and in the village **King Arthur's Great Halls** are another popular attraction, telling the story and Arthur and his retinue in displays, sound, music and laser lights. The cliffs on which the Castle stand are at the heart of a Site of Special Scientific Interest. In a small 14 th century manor house in the centre of Tintagel stands the **Old Post Office**, which was one of the National Trust's first acquisitions, being purchased for £100 in 1903.

Trebetherick

The simple, delightful **Church of St Enedoc** lies among dunes in the shadow of Brea Hill. The churchyard contains the graves of many mariners whose ships came to grief in the dangerous waters on this

Trevose Head

At the tip of this remote headland stands **Trevose Lighthouse**, with a powerful beam that reaches 20 miles out to sea. At night, lights from four other lighthouses can be seen from this spot on the 200ft granite cliffs.

Wadebridge

Standing at the historic lowest bridging point of the River Camel, this ancient port and busy market town is also a popular choice for a holiday. The town's former railway station is now home to the **John Betjeman Centre** dedicated to the life and work of the much-loved Poet Laureate. The railway disappeared in the 1960s, but a stretch of the trackbed was used to create the superb **Camel Trail**, part of a network of walking and cycling routes covering Cornwall.

1 Airways Hotel

Little Carloggas, St Mawgan, Cornwall TR8 4EQ
Tel: 01637 860595

Real Ales, Bar Food, Restaurant Menu,
Accommodation, No Smoking Area, Disabled Facilities

2 Atlantic House Hotel

New Polzeath, Wadebridge, Cornwall PL27 6UG
Tel: 01208 862208

Real Ales, Bar Food, Restaurant Menu,
Accommodation, No Smoking Area

3 Barley Sheaf Hotel

2 Lower Bore Street, Bodmin, Cornwall PL31 2JR
Tel: 01208 72716

Real Ales, Bar Food, Accommodation,
No Smoking Area

4 Bettle and Chisel Inn

High Street, Delabole, Camelford,
Cornwall PL33 9AQ
Tel: 01840 211402

Real Ales, Bar Food, Restaurant Menu,
Accommodation, No Smoking Area

5 Blisland Inn

The Green, Blisland, Cornwall PL30 4JF
Tel: 01208 850739

Real Ales, Bar Food, Restaurant Menu,
No Smoking Area, Disabled Facilities

6 Bodmin Jail

Berrycombe Rd, Bodmin, Cornwall PL31 2NR
Tel: 01208 76292

Real Ales, Restaurant Menu, No Smoking Area,
Disabled Facilities

7 Borough Arms

Dunmere, Bodmin, Cornwall PL31 2RD
Tel: 01208 73118

Real Ales, Bar Food, Restaurant Menu,
No Smoking Area, Disabled Facilities

8 Bossiney House Hotel

Bossiney, Tintagel, Cornwall PL34 0AX
Tel: 01840 770240

Restaurant Menu, Accommodation, No Smoking Area,
Disabled Facilities

9 Bridge On Wool

The Platt, Wadebridge, Cornwall PL27 7AQ
Tel: 01208 812750

Real Ales, Disabled Facilities

10 Carpenters Arms

Polzeath, Wadebridge, Cornwall PL27 6TL
Tel: 01208 863579

Real Ales, Bar Food, Restaurant Menu,
No Smoking Area, Disabled Facilities

11 The Cat and Fiddle

1 St Leonards, Bodmin, Cornwall PL31 1JZ
Tel: 01208 77764

Real Ales, Bar Food, No Smoking Area,
Disabled Facilities

12 **Cornish Arms**

Pendoggett, Port Isaac, Bodmin,
Cornwall PL30 3HH
Tel: 01208 880263

Real Ales, Bar Food, Restaurant Menu,
Accommodation, No Smoking Area

See panel opposite

13 Cornish Arms Inn

Churchtown Avenue, St Merryn, Padstow,
Cornwall PL28 8ND
Tel: 01841 520288

Real Ales, Bar Food, Restaurant Menu,
No Smoking Area, Disabled Facilities

14 Cornishman Inn

Fore Street, Tintagal, Cornwall PL34 0DB
Tel: 01840 770238

Real Ales, Bar Food, Restaurant Menu,
Accommodation, No Smoking Area, Disabled Facilities

12 The Cornish Arms

Pendoggett, nr Port Isaac, Cornwall PL30 3HH
☎ 01208 880263 Fax: 01208880335
🌐 www.cornisharms.com
e-mail: info@cornisharms.com

Real Ales, Bar Food, Restaurant Menu, Accommodation, No Smoking Area

☞ Leave the A39 at St Teath for minor road to B3314; left on to B3314, then 1½ miles to Pendoggett

🍺 3 or 4 Sharp's brews

🍴 Traditional and Thai dishes; must book

🛏 7 en suite rooms

🎵 Pool table

⛰ Car park, garden with sea views

💳 All the major cards

🕐 11-11

🏛 Port Gaverne 1 mile, Port Isaac 2 miles, St Endellion 1 mile, Polzeath 4 miles, Padstow 7 miles, Eden Project 40 mins

Just minutes from the main A39, **The Cornish Arms**, which has a 3 diamond rating from the English Tourist Board, excels both as a restaurant and as place to stay. The bars at this outstanding free house are warm and inviting, with a friendly, relaxed ambience for sampling the excellent Sharp's real ales. There's a pool and darts area, and in warm weather outside tables make the most of the pleasant setting. The great selection of home cooking includes pub classics, super seafood and authentic Thai dishes available daily in the bars or dining room. Local produce is used whenever possible.

Seven en suite bedrooms provide an excellent standard of accommodation and an ideal base for exploring. Close to several golf courses including Bowood, Trevose, Lanhydrock and the testing St Enodoc. Special golf breaks can be arranged.

15 Crow's Nest

4 The Terrace, Port Isaac, Cornwall PL29 3SG
Tel: 01208 880305

Real Ales, Bar Food, Accommodation, No Smoking Area

16 Darlington Inn

Fore Street, Camelford, Cornwall PL32 9PG
Tel: 01840 213314

Real Ales, Bar Food, Restaurant Menu, Accommodation, No Smoking Area

17 Earl of St Vincent

Egloshayle, Wadebridge, Cornwall PL27 6HT
Tel: 01208 814807

Real Ales, Bar Food, Restaurant Menu, No Smoking Area, Disabled Facilities

18 Falcon Inn

St Mawgan, Newquay, Cornwall TR8 4EP
Tel: 01637 860225

Real Ales, Bar Food, Restaurant Menu, Accommodation, No Smoking Area, Disabled Facilities

19 Farmers Arms

St Merryn, Padstow, Cornwall PL28 8NP
Tel: 01841 520303

Real Ales, Bar Food, Restaurant Menu, Accommodation, No Smoking Area, Disabled Facilities

20 Four Ways Inn

Churchtown Avenue, St Minver, Wadebridge, Cornwall PL27 6QH
Tel: 01208 862384

Real Ales, Bar Food, Restaurant Menu, Accommodation, No Smoking Area

21 The Garland Ox Inn
65 Higher Bore Street, Bodmin, Cornwall PL31 1JS
Tel: 01208 75372
Real Ales

22 Golden Lion
Fore Street, Port Isaac, Cornwall PL29 3RB
Tel: 01208 880336
Real Ales, Bar Food, Restaurant Menu

23 Golden Lion Hotel
Lanadwell St, Padstow, Cornwall PL28 8AN
Tel: 01841 532797
Real Ales, Bar Food, Accommodation,
No Smoking Area

24 Halfway House Inn
Charlottes Place, St Jidgey, Wadebridge,
Cornwall PL27 7RE
Tel: 01208 812524
Real Ales, Bar Food, Restaurant Menu,
No Smoking Area, Disabled Facilities

25 Harbour Inn
Strand Street, South Quay, Padstow,
Cornwall PL28 8BL
Tel: 01841 533148
Real Ales, Bar Food, Restaurant Menu,
No Smoking Area, Disabled Facilities

26 Harlyn Inn
Harlyn Bay, Padstow, Cornwall PL28 8SB
Tel: 01841 520207
Real Ales, Bar Food, Restaurant Menu,
Accommodation, No Smoking Area, Disabled Facilities

27 The Hole In The Wall
Crockwell Street, Bodmin, Cornwall PL31 2DS
Tel: 01208 72397
Real Ales, Restaurant Menu, No Smoking Area,
Disabled Facilities

28 King Arthur's Castle Hotel
Tintagel, Cornwall PL34 0DQ
Tel: 01840 770202
Real Ales, Bar Food, Accommodation,
No Smoking Area

29 Lanivet Inn
Truro Rd, Lanivet , Bodmin, Cornwall PL30 5ET
Tel: 01208 831212
Real Ales, Bar Food, Restaurant Menu,
No Smoking Area, Disabled Facilities

30 London Inn
6-8 Lanadwell Street, Padstow, Cornwall PL28 8AN
Tel: 01841 532554
Real Ales, Bar Food, Restaurant Menu,
Accommodation, Disabled Facilities

31 Maltsters Arms
Chapel Amble, Wadebridge, Cornwall PL27 6EU
Tel: 01208 812473
Real Ales, Bar Food, Restaurant Menu,
No Smoking Area

32 Mariners Rock
Slipway Rock, Wadebridge, Cornwall PL27 6LD
Tel: 01208 863679
Real Ales, Bar Food, Restaurant Menu,
Accommodation, No Smoking Area, Disabled Facilities

33 Masons Arms
5/9 Higher Bore St, Bodmin, Cornwall PL31 1JS
Tel: 01208 72607
Real Ales, Bar Food, Restaurant Menu,
No Smoking Area, Disabled Facilities

34 Masons Arms
Market Place, Camelford, Cornwall PL32 9PB
Tel: 01840 213309
Real Ales, Restaurant Menu, Accommodation,
No Smoking Area

35 The Merrymoor Inn

Mawgan Porth, nr Newquay, Cornwall TR8 4BA

☎ 1637 860258 ⊕ www.merrymoorinn.com

Real Ales, Bar Food, Accommodation,
No Smoking Area, Disabled Facilities

☛ From the A30 take the A392 to Newquay and
the B3276 coast road to Mawgan Porth

🍺 Selection

🍴 Lunch & Dinner, all day in summer

🛏 7 en suite rooms

♪ Regular winter quiz

⚓ Extensive gardens and grounds, car park

💳 Major cards accepted

🕐 11-11 (Sun to 10.30)

🏛 Newquay 4 miles, St Mawgan 1 mile, Trevose
Head 6 miles

Built in the 1930s, the **Merrymoor Inn** is set in lovely grounds covering about an acre. With gardens at the front and standing just 100 yards from the beach at Mawgan

Porth, this family-run inn offers picturesque views in all directions.

Lynne and Dudley Bennett, who have been at the helm for nearly 40 years, have made many improvements down the years, including the creation of a beer garden and extending the family areas. Good food, well-kept ales and comfortable accommodation have long been bywords here, and the family facilities and the great views are bonuses that add to the attraction of the inn.

Home-cooked meals are supervised by Lynne, who guarantees that everything from

sandwiches to main courses are expertly prepared and absolutely delicious. Bar snacks and meals are available lunchtime and evening every day, and all day in summer, and there's a popular carvery on Sundays and every day in July and August. Booking is recommended for Sunday lunch and other meals in high season. To accompany a meal or to enjoy on their own, the Merrymoor Inn stocks a good selection of real ales (usually four), lagers, ciders, wines, spirits and soft drinks.

Mawgan Porth lies on a particularly impressive stretch of coastline, and the inn provides a very pleasant, civilised base for a holiday by the sea, with easy access to places of historic and scenic interest inland. The guest accommodation comprises seven en suite rooms (5 doubles, a twin and a single), all handsomely decorated and furnished and most enjoying superb views of the bay. Lynne and Dudley have a warm welcome for all their visitors – the more the merrier at the Merrymoor Inn!

35 Merrymoor Inn

Mawgan Porth, Newquay, Cornwall TR8 4BA
Tel: 01637 860258

Real Ales, Bar Food, Accommodation,
No Smoking Area, Disabled Facilities

See panel on page 63

36 The Mill House Inn

Tintagel, Cornwall PL34 0HD
Tel: 01840 770200

Real Ales, Bar Food, Restaurant Menu,
Accommodation

37 Molesworth Arms Hotel

Molesworth Street, Wadebridge,
Cornwall PL27 7DP
Tel: 01208 812055

Real Ales, Bar Food, Restaurant Menu,
Accommodation, No Smoking Area, Disabled Facilities

38 Napoleon Inn

High Street, Boscastle, Cornwall PL35 0BD
Tel: 01840 250204

Real Ales, Bar Food, Restaurant Menu,
No Smoking Area

39 Newlands Hotel

Main Road, Trevone, Padstow, Cornwall PL28 8QX
Tel: 01841 520469

Restaurant Menu, Accommodation, No Smoking Area

40 Old Custom House Hotel

South Quay, Padstow, Cornwall PL28 8BL
Tel: 01841 532359

Real Ales, Bar Food, Restaurant Menu,
Accommodation, No Smoking Area, Disabled Facilities

42 The Old School Hotel & Restaurant

Fore Street, Port Isaac, Cornwall PL29 3RD

☎ 01208 880721

⊕ www.cornwall-on-line.co.uk/old-school-hotel

Restaurant Menu, Accommodation,
No Smoking Area

☛ Overlooking the harbour in Port Isaac at the
end of the B3267 5 miles N of Wadebridge

🍴 12-2.30 & 7-9.30

🛏 15 en suite rooms

⚓ Terrace has sea views

💳 Major cards except Amex

🚫 Non-smoking bedrooms

🕐 Open all day

🏛 Port Gaverne 1 mile, Long Cross Gardens 1
mile, Polzeath 2 miles, Wadebridge 6 miles

Built in 1875, the **Old School** retains much
Victorian charm while offering modern
style and comfort. This outstanding hotel and
restaurant is in the very capable hands of
owner Louise Houston, and a warm welcome
from Louise and her staff is guaranteed. The
accommodation (B&B or Dinner, B&B)
comprises 15 beautifully appointed rooms
ranging from singles to suites. The bar and
lounge are delightful places to unwind, and in
the restaurant chef Jake Pattenden's menus use
the best seasonal produce in cooked-to-order
dishes that cater for both traditional and more
adventurous tastes. The delights of coast and
countryside are on the doorstep, and the
unspoilt fishing village of Port Isaac is well
worth taking time to explore. The energetic
can undertake the two-hour hike along the
South West Coast Path to Port Quinn.

41 Old Inn and Restaurant

Churchtown, St Breward, Bodmin Moor,
Cornwall PL30 4PP
Tel: 01208 850711

Real Ales, Bar Food, Restaurant Menu,
No Smoking Area, Disabled Facilities

42 Old School Hotel and Restaurant

Fore Street, Port Isaac, Cornwall PL29 3RD
Tel: 01208 880721

Restaurant Menu, Accommodation, No Smoking Area

See panel opposite

43 Old Ship Hotel

Mill Square, Padstow, Cornwall PL28 8AE
Tel: 01841 532357

Real Ales, Bar Food, Restaurant Menu,
Accommodation, No Smoking Area, Disabled Facilities

44 Oyster Catcher Bar & Holiday Apartment

Polzeath, Cornwall PL27 6TG
Tel: 01208 862371

Real Ales, Bar Food, Restaurant Menu,
Accommodation, Disabled Facilities

45 The Phoenix

Watergate Bay, Newquay, Cornwall TR8 4AB
Tel: 01637 860353

Real Ales, Bar Food, Restaurant Menu,
No Smoking Area, Disabled Facilities

46 The Pickwick Inn

St Issey, Nr Padstow, Cornwall PL27 7QQ
Tel: 01841 540361

Real Ales, Bar Food, Restaurant Menu,
No Smoking Area, Disabled Facilities

47 Poldark Inn

Delabole, Camelford, Cornwall PL33 9DQ
Tel: 01840 212565

Real Ales, Bar Food, Accommodation,
Disabled Facilities

48 Port Gaverne Hotel

Port Gaverne, Port Isaac, Cornwall PL29 3SQ
Tel: 01208 880244

Real Ales, Bar Food, Restaurant Menu,
Accommodation, No Smoking Area

49 Port William Inn

Trebarwith Strand Village, Nr Tintagel,
Cornwall PL34 0HB
Tel: 01840 770230

Real Ales, Bar Food, Restaurant Menu,
Accommodation, No Smoking Area, Disabled Facilities

50 Quarryman Inn

Edmonton, Wadebridge, Cornwall PL27 7JA
Tel: 01208 816444

Real Ales, Bar Food, Restaurant Menu,
Accommodation, No Smoking Area

51 Ring O'Bells

Churchtown Avenue, St Issey, Wadebridge,
Cornwall PL27 7QA
Tel: 01841 540251

Real Ales, Bar Food, Restaurant Menu,
Accommodation, No Smoking Area

52 The Riv

Mawgan Porth, Newquay, Cornwall TR8 4BA
Tel: 01637 860177

Real Ales, Bar Food, Restaurant Menu,
No Smoking Area, Disabled Facilities

53 Rock Inn Bar and Bistro

Wadebridge, Cornwall PL27 6LD
Tel: 01208 863498

Real Ales, Bar Food

54 Seascape Hotel

Polzeath, Nr Wadebridge, Cornwall PL27 6SX
Tel: 01208 863638

Real Ales, Restaurant Menu, Accommodation,
No Smoking Area, Disabled Facilities

61 St Mabyn Inn

St Mabyn, nr Bodmin, Cornwall PL30 3BA
☎ 01208 841266

Real Ales, Bar Food, Restaurant Menu,
No Smoking Area

- St Mabyn is found on minor roads off the A39 2 miles E of Wadebridge
- Sharps
- 12-2.30 & 6-9.30
- Seats outside
- Major cards except Amex & Diners
- 11-11
- Wadebridge 2 miles, Bodmin 6 miles

St Mabyn is a picturesque village east of Wadebridge off the A39, named after St Mabyn, a saintly lady who was one of 24 children of a 5th century Welsh king called Brychan Brycheiniog. Close to the Church that also carries the saint's name, the **St Mabyn Inn** dates from the 17th century, beginning life as a farmhouse before becoming the cosy, popular inn is it today, a handsome white-shuttered brick building.

The place is a real ale lover's paradise, open all day every day for the sale of four real ales, which rises to six in the summer months. Among the regular brews are Sharps Doom Bar, Cornish Coaster and Special, plus Bass and a guest that usually comes from a local micro-brewery. The bar also stocks a fine range of other beers, lagers, ciders, wines, spirits and soft drinks. The bar itself is full of inviting, old-world charm, with plenty of dark wood and framed prints. At one end is a pool table.

Mine hosts are Jane and Gary, who created a pub that would be a credit and a valued asset to any village. Food is served between 12 and 2.30 and 6 to 9.30 daily, either in the bar or in the comfortable 40-cover non-smoking restaurant. Jane is a great cook, offering a splendid choice on the regular menu and the daily changing specials board. Lunchtime favourites include steak & kidney pie, lamb chops and lasagne, and steaks served sizzling with all the trimmings are particularly popular. Traditional roasts are added to the Sunday menu, and booking is recommended for this, and for all meals in high season.

This really super inn is definitely a place to seek out in this delightful part of the world, where visitors can enjoy the beautiful countryside, stately homes and lovely gardens, and the amenities and history of Wadebridge and Bodmin.

55 The Ship Inn
Gonvena Hill, Wadebridge, Cornwall PL27 6DF
Tel: 01208 812839

Real Ales, Bar Food, Restaurant Menu,
No Smoking Area

56 Shipwrights
North Quay, Padstow, Cornwall PL28 8AF
Tel: 01841 532451

Real Ales, Bar Food, Restaurant Menu,
No Smoking Area

57 Slades House Country Inn
Sladesbridge, Wadebridge, Cornwall PL27 6JB
Tel: 01208 812729

Real Ales, Bar Food, Accommodation,
No Smoking Area

58 Slipway Hotel
The Harbour Front, Port Isaac, Cornwall PL29 3RH
Tel: 01208 880264

Real Ales, Bar Food, Restaurant Menu,
Accommodation, No Smoking Area, Disabled Facilities

59 The Spinning Wheel
Bridge Walk The Bridge, Boscastle,
Cornwall PL35 0HE
Tel: 01840 250501

Restaurant Menu, No Smoking Area,
Disabled Facilities

60 St Enodoc Hotel
Rock, Wadebridge, Cornwall PL27 6LA
Tel: 01208 863394

Real Ales, Restaurant Menu, Accommodation,
No Smoking Area, Disabled Facilities

61 St Mabyn Inn
Churchtown, St Mabyn, Cornwall PL30 3BA
Tel: 01208 841266

Real Ales, Bar Food, Restaurant Menu,
No Smoking Area

See panel opposite

62 Tintagel Arms Hotel
Fore Street, Tintagel, Cornwall PL34 0DB
Tel: 01840 770780

Real Ales, Bar Food, Accommodation,
Disabled Facilities

63 Travellers Rest
Trevarrian, St Mawgan, Cornwall TR8 4AQ
Tel: 01637 860245

Real Ales, Bar Food, Restaurant Menu,
No Smoking Area, Disabled Facilities

64 Tredrea Inn
Porthcothan Bay, Padstow, Cornwall PL28 8LN
Tel: 01841 520450

Real Ales, Bar Food, Restaurant Menu,
No Smoking Area, Disabled Facilities

See panel below

64 Tredrea Inn
Porthcothan Bay, nr Padstow, Cornwall PL28 8LN
☎ 01841 520450

**Real Ales, Bar Food, Restaurant Menu,
No Smoking Area, Disabled Facilities**

- By the B3276 coastal road at Porthcothan Bay, 5 miles from Padstow
- Doom Bar, Betty Stoggs
- 12-3 & 6-9
- Children's playroom, garden, car park
- Major cards accepted
- 11-11 (Sun 12-10.30)
- South West Coast Path; Padstow 5 miles, Newquay 8 miles

A scenic setting above Porthcothan Bay is just one of the assets of the **Tredrea Inn**, and the views from the lawned garden are stunning. Leaseholder Adrian Olsen, ably assisted by bar managers Milly and Kev, chefs Dave, Dan and Don, and waitresses Paula and Anna, provide the pub's many visitors with hospitality, real ales from local breweries and a wide-ranging menu that includes super fresh fish dishes. This family-friendly inn has a separate children's play room.

65 Tregurrian Hotel

Watergate Bay, Newquay, Cornwall TR8 4AB
Tel: 01637 860280

Real Ales, Bar Food, Restaurant Menu,
Accommodation, No Smoking Area, Disabled Facilities

66 The Weavers

Honey Street, Bodmin, Cornwall PL31 2DL
Tel: 01208 74511

Real Ales, Bar Food, Restaurant Menu,
No Smoking Area, Disabled Facilities

67 Well Parc Inn

Dobbin Lane, Trevone, Padstow,
Cornwall PL28 8QN
Tel: 01841 520318

Real Ales, Bar Food, Accommodation,
No Smoking Area, Disabled Facilities

68 The Wellington Hotel

Old Road, Boscastle, Cornwall PL35 0AQ
Tel: 01840 250202

Real Ales, Bar Food, Restaurant Menu,
Accommodation, No Smoking Area

69 Wootons Country Hotel

Fore Street, Tintagel, Cornwall PL34 0DA
Tel: 01840 770170

Real Ales, Bar Food, Restaurant Menu,
Accommodation, No Smoking Area

70 Ye Olde Malthouse

Fore Street, Tintagel, Cornwall PL34 0DA
Tel: 01840 770461

Real Ales, Bar Food, Restaurant Menu,
Accommodation

See panel below

70 Ye Olde Malthouse

Fore Street, Tintagel, Cornwall PL34 0DA
☎ 01840 770461
🌐 www.yeoldmalthouseinn.com

Real Ales, Bar Food, Restaurant Menu,
Accommodation

☛ From the A30 2 miles W of Launceston take the A395, then A39. Just before Camelford take B road signed to Tintagel

🍺 Sharps, Skinners, St Austell, Ring o Bells

🍴 10.30-9

🛏 7 rooms

🅿 Patio, car park

💳 Major cards except Diners

🕐 10.30am – 11pm

🏛 Boscastle 3 miles, Camelford 4 miles

The historic village of Tintagel is filled with myths and legends, but one fact that cannot be denied is that Ye Olde Malthouse is one of the very best inns in Cornwall. It's also one of the oldest, with parts of the mellow whitewashed building dating back to the 14th century. Up to four real ales from local breweries are available, and superb food is served throughout the day, in the bar, the non-smoking restaurant or, weather permitting, on the patio overlooking St Materiana's Church. Given its location, it's not surprising that seafood is a speciality, and much of the produce is brought in daily from nearby Port Isaac. There's also a good choice for meat-eaters and vegetarians, and preparation and presentation are both given great care and attention. And with seven comfortable guest bedrooms, Ye Olde Malthouse is also an ideal base for a holiday in the midst of history and glorious scenery.

MID CORNWALL SOUTH

The mining heritage is particularly strong in St Austell, where the famous brewery is a magnet for connoisseurs of the finest cask ales. One mining site has been converted into the world famous Eden Project, one of the country's major visitor attractions, while more traditional gardening methods can be seen at the extraordinary Lost Gardens of Heligan. The maritime legacy can be experienced at Charlestown and Polperro, while literary connections are very strong in Fowey.

Bodinnick

Close to the slipway in this attractive coastal hamlet stands the house where Daphne du Maurier wrote her first novel, *The Loving Spirit*. Sir Arthur Quiller Couch ('Q') is remembered by a monolithic memorial at Penleath Point.

Bodinnick

Carlyon Bay

An up-to-date seaside resort almost at the centre of the long, sweeping St Austell Bay.

Carthew

Just south of the tiny village of Carthew, 2 miles north of St Austell, is the **Wheal Martin China Clay Museum**, an open-air museum that tells the 200-year story of one of Cornwall's most important industries.

Charlestown

In a historic clay building close to the docks, the **Charlestown Shipwreck & Heritage Centre** provides visitors with a fascinating insight into the town's history, local shipwrecks and the many devices developed down the years for rescuing those in peril on the sea.

Section 4

Indian Queens
75
48
56
6

15 21
30 54
58 59

36
Lostwithiel
11

Section 7

Duloe
78

Nanpean
4
23

33

62
Carthew
27

51
Lanreath

Foxhole
32

9
St Blazey
44
Tregrehan
Mills
39
18 5
76

16

66

28

2
St Austell
Section 2
74
25 49

26
8
46 50
Carlyon Bay
Charlestown
45
57
68
Par
53
Fowey
37
60

Bodinnick
42

Porthallow
12 71

Polperro
3 40
43 47
65 72

13

Pentewan
7 14
41 52
63 77
69

19 20
22 29
38 61
67

Section 8

34
Tregony
17
Mevagissey
10

24 31
55 64
73

Portmellon

Goran
35

Portloe
70

---

11 Pub or Inn Reference Number - Detailed Information

12 Pub or Inn Reference Number - Summary Entry

●■ Place of interest mentioned in the chapter introduction

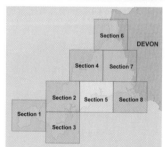

Fowey

A lovely old seafaring town guarding the entrance to the river from which it takes its name. The town and the area have many notable literary connections: next to the **Church of St Finnbar** is the **Daphne du Maurier Literary Centre**, while on the esplanade stands **The Haven**, the home of Sir Arthur Quiller Couch, a Cambridge professor and sometime Mayor of Fowey who wrote under the pen name of Q.

Mevagissey

Indian Queens

This curiously named, chiefly Victorian village is the location of the **Screech Owl Sanctuary**, home to the largest collection of owls and other birds of prey in the Southwest.

Lanreath

This pretty village with cob cottages at its centre is home to the **Lanreath Folk and Farm Museum** housed in an old tithe barn. Exhibits include old implements, mill workings, engines, tractors, craft workshops and a traditional farmhouse kitchen.

Lostwithiel

The capital of Cornwall in the 13th century and one of the historic stannary towns, Lostwithiel retains many reminders of its past in its buildings: the **Great Hall**, which served as the treasury and stannary offices; the **Guildhall**, now home to **LostwithielMuseum**; the 16th century **Taprell House**; the striking **St Bartholomew's Church** that relate to the close links between the Celts of Cornwall and those of northern France.

Mevagissey

The attractions of this, the largest fishing village in St Austell Bay, are many and varied. The harbour is home to the town's **Museum**, where the exhibits include the pilchard industry, old agricultural machinery and the story behind Pears Soap, which was developed locally. There are more than 2,000 models and 40 trains in the **World of Model Railways Exhibition** in Meadow Street.

Par

The harbour here was built in the 1840s as part of the expansion of the china clay industry, and the slender chimneys of the clay processing plant can be seen from Par

Sands. At low tide the flat beach can extend half a mile out to sea, and the dunes and lagoons behind the beach are particularly rich in wildlife.

Pentewan

Inland from this village, long famous for its stone, lie the **Lost Gardens of Heligan**, gardens originally laid out in 1780 and

Lost Gardens of Heligan

restored after being rediscovered in 1990. Following one of the largest garden restoration projects in the world, these amazing gardens are a real living museum of late-18th and 19th century horticulture.

Polperro

All roads in Polperro lead down to the harbour, and while the village was centuries dependent on the pilchard fishing industry, it also has a long association with the less public industry of smuggling. Both aspects are explored in the **Polperro Museum of Smuggling and Fishing**.

St Austell

The mining of tin, copper and china clay once dominated this old market town, and the spoil heaps, softened down the years, caused the area to be known as the Cornish Alps. Another, still important local industry is brewing, and the **St Austell Brewery Visitor Centre** offers a guided tour that includes a sample of the traditional cask-conditioned ales.

St Blazey

The site of the world famous **Eden Project**, where the largest conservatories (biodomes) in the world promote the understanding and responsible management of the vital relationship between plants, people and resources. The plants come from all over the world and are grown in conditions that cover the whole range of temperatures and environments.

Tregrehan Mills

In the 19th century **Tregrehan Gardens** visitors can see mature trees from around the world, superb rhododendrons and Carlyon hybrid camellias. The glasshouses date from 1846, and the house has been in the Carlyon family since 1565.

1 The Barley Sheaf

Gorran Churchtown, Nr Mevagissey, St Austell,
Cornwall PL26 6HN
Tel: 01726 843330

Real Ales, Bar Food, Restaurant Menu,
No Smoking Area, Disabled Facilities

2 The Bell

Trewoon, St Austell, Cornwall PL25 5TQ
Tel: 01726 68047

Real Ales, Bar Food, Restaurant Menu,
Accommodation, No Smoking Area

3 Blue Peter Inn

Quay Road, Polperro, Looe, Cornwall PL13 2QZ
Tel: 01503 272743

Real Ales, Bar Food, Restaurant Menu,
No Smoking Area

4 Boscawen Hotel

Fore Street, St Dennis, Nr St Austel,
Cornwall PL26 8AD
Tel: 01726 822275

Real Ales, Bar Food, Restaurant Menu,
Accommodation, No Smoking Area, Disabled Facilities

5 Britannia Inn

St Austell Road, Par, Cornwall PL24 2SL
Tel: 01726 812889

Real Ales, Bar Food, Restaurant Menu,
No Smoking Area, Disabled Facilities

6 Bugle Inn

57 Fore Street, Bugle, St Austell,
Cornwall PL26 8PB
Tel: 01726 850307

Real Ales, Bar Food, Restaurant Menu,
Accommodation, No Smoking Area

See panel below

6 The Bugle Inn

Fore Street, Bugle, Cornwall PL26 8PB
☎ 01726 850307   ⊕ www.bugleinn.co.uk

**Real Ales, Bar Food, Restaurant Menu,
Accommodation, No Smoking Area**

☞ 4 miles north of St Austell on the A391 road to Bodmin

☕ 4 real ales from the St Austell Brewery

🍴 Bar meals

🛏 5 rooms for B&B

🎵 Quiz Wednesday; live music Sunday

🅿 Car park

💳 Major cards

🏅 Finalist in Cask Ales and Floral Display competitions

🕐 11-11

🏛 Roche Rock & Hermitage 2 miles, Eden Project 3 miles

The Bugle Inn is a handsome stone building on the corner of Fore Street and Roche Road. Simon and Pam Rodger, here for 12 years, welcome friends old and new into the cosy, homely interior, and the owners and their staff generate a very happy and relaxed atmosphere.

Four cask ales from the St Austell Brewery head the list of liquid refreshment, and the food – available throughout the day – runs from snacks to full meals, with classics such as pasties, pies and seafood specials among the favourites. Five rooms are open all year for Bed & Breakfast guests at the Bugle, which gave its name to the village, which was once a centre of the clay-mining industry.

7 Carlyon Arms

Sandy Hill, St Austell, Cornwall PL25 3AS
Tel: 01726 72129

Real Ales, Bar Food, Restaurant Menu,
No Smoking Area, Disabled Facilities

8 Cliff Head Hotel

Sea Road, Carlyon Bay, St Austell,
Cornwall PL25 3RB
Tel: 01726 812345

Real Ales, Bar Food, Restaurant Menu,
Accommodation, No Smoking Area

9 The Cornish Arms

Church Street, St Blazey, , Cornwall PL24 2NG
Tel: 01726 813001

Real Ales, Bar Food, Restaurant Menu,
Accommodation, No Smoking Area, Disabled Facilities

10 Crown Inn

Church Town, St Ewe, Nr St Austell,
Cornwall PL26 6UY
Tel: 01726 843322

Real Ales, Bar Food, Accommodation,
No Smoking Area, Disabled Facilities

11 Crown Inn

Lanlivery, Bodmin, Cornwall PL30 5BT
Tel: 01208 872707

Real Ales, Bar Food, Restaurant Menu,
Accommodation, No Smoking Area, Disabled Facilities

12 The Crumplehorn Inn

Crumplehorn, Polperro, Looe, Cornwall PL13 2RJ
Tel: 01503 272348

Real Ales, Bar Food, Restaurant Menu,
Accommodation, No Smoking Area, Disabled Facilities

13 Dolphin Inn

Fore Street, Grampound, Truro, Cornwall TR2 4RR
Tel: 01726 882435

Real Ales, Bar Food, Restaurant Menu,
No Smoking Area, Disabled Facilities

14 Duke of Cornwall Hotel

98 Victoria Road, St Austell, Cornwall PL25 4QD
Tel: 01726 72031

Real Ales, Bar Food, Restaurant Menu,
Accommodation, No Smoking Area, Disabled Facilities

15 Earl of Chatham

Grenville Road, Lostwithiel, Cornwall PL22 0EP
Tel: 01208 872269

Real Ales, Bar Food, Accommodation,
Disabled Facilities

16 Fishermans Arms

Fore Street, Golant, Fowey, Cornwall PL23 1LN
Tel: 01726 832453

Real Ales, Bar Food

17 Fountain Inn

Cliff Street, Mevagissey, St Austell,
Cornwall PL26 6QB
Tel: 01726 842320

Real Ales, Bar Food, Restaurant Menu,
Accommodation, No Smoking Area

18 The Four Lords

St Austell Road, St Blazey Gate, Par,
Cornwall PL24 2EE
Tel: 01726 814200

Real Ales, Bar Food, Restaurant Menu

19 Fowey Hotel

The Esplanade, Fowey, Cornwall PL23 1HX
Tel: 01726 832551

Real Ales, Bar Food, Restaurant Menu,
Accommodation, No Smoking Area, Disabled Facilities

20 Galleon Inn

12 Fore Street, Fowey, Cornwall PL23 1AQ
Tel: 01726 833014

Real Ales, Bar Food, Restaurant Menu,
Accommodation, No Smoking Area, Disabled Facilities

21 Globe Inn

North Street, Lostwithiel, Cornwall PL22 0EG
Tel: 01208 872501

Real Ales, Bar Food, Restaurant Menu,
Accommodation, No Smoking Area, Disabled Facilities

22 Globe Posting House Hotel

19 Fore Steet, Fowey, Cornwall PL23 1AH
Tel: 01726 833322

Real Ales, Restaurant Menu, Accommodation,
No Smoking Area

23 The Grenville Arms
Fore Street, Nanpean, Nr St Austell,
Cornwall PL26 7YE Tel: 01726 823692
Bar Food, No Smoking Area, Disabled Facilities

24 Harbour Tavern
Jetty Street, Mevagissey, St Austell,
Cornwall PL26 6UH
Tel: 01726 842220

Real Ales, Bar Food, Restaurant Menu,
Accommodation, No Smoking Area, Disabled Facilities

See panel below

25 Hewas Inn
Fore Street, Sticker, St Austell, Cornwall PL26 7HD
Tel: 01726 73497

Real Ales, Bar Food, Restaurant Menu,
No Smoking Area, Disabled Facilities

See panel on page 76

26 Holmbush Inn
Holmbush Road, St Austell, Cornwall PL25 3LL
Tel: 01726 68691

Real Ales, Bar Food, No Smoking Area,
Disabled Facilities

27 Innis Inn
Innis Moor, Penwithick, St Austell,
Cornwall PL26 8YH
Tel: 01726 851162

Bar Food, Restaurant Menu, Accommodation,
No Smoking Area, Disabled Facilities

28 Jubilee Inn
Jubilee Hill, Pelynt, Nr Looe, Cornwall PL13 2JZ
Tel: 01503 220312

Real Ales, Bar Food, Restaurant Menu,
Accommodation, No Smoking Area, Disabled Facilities

29 King of Prussia Hotel
Town Quay, Fowey, Cornwall PL23 1AT
Tel: 01726 833694

Real Ales, Bar Food, Restaurant Menu,
Accommodation, No Smoking Area, Disabled Facilities

30 Kings Arms
Fore Street, Lostwithiel, Cornwall PL22 0BL
Tel: 01208 872383

Real Ales, Accommodation

24 The Harbour Tavern
Jetty Street, Mevagissey, Cornwall PL26 6UH
☎ 01726 842220   ⊕ www.mevagissey.net

**Real Ales, Bar Food, Restaurant Menu, Accommo-
dation, No Smoking Area, Disabled Facilities**

- ☛ On the harbourfront in Mevagissey, 5 miles
south of St Austell on the B3273
- 🍺 3 Skinner's ales
- 🍴 Home cooked dishes served all day
- 🛏 3 rooms en suite + separate apartment
- 🕐 8am-11pm
- 🏛 Gorran Haven 2 miles, St Austell 5 miles, Lost
Gardens of Heligan 2 miles

The Harbour Tavern enjoys a fine location
right on the harbourfront in the bustling
village of Mevagissey. Hosts Chris and
Susannah Macklin have made a superb job of
updating this handsome stone and slate inn,
whose origins go back to the 14th century.

In high season, the scene outside the pub is
one of colourful activity on the water, and at
any time of year the Harbour Tavern is an
excellent place for enjoying Cornish ales and
ciders and food that includes fish and shellfish
freshly landed in the harbour.

With three top-class en suite rooms and a
self-contained apartment, the inn is also an
ideal base for discovering the many delights of
the area, including bracing walks, stunning
scenery, sandy beaches and the renowned Lost
Gardens of Heligan.

25 The Hewas Inn

Fore Street, Sticker, nr St Austell,
Cornwall PL26 7HD
☎ 01726 73497

Real Ales, Bar Food, Restaurant Menu,
No Smoking Area, Disabled Facilities

- ☛ Off the A390 2 miles SW of St Austell
- 🍺 4 or 5 from St Austell Brewery
- 🍴 12-2 & 6-9
- 🎵 Sunday quiz
- 🚗 Car park, patio
- 💳 Major cards except Amex
- 🕐 12-2 & 6-11
- 🏛 St Austell 2 miles, Lost Gardens of Heligan 4 miles, Mevagissey 5 miles, Probus Gardens & Trewithen 6 miles

Edgcumbe Arms at Cremyll.

Licensed as an inn from the time it was built in 1730, the Hewas Inn (Hewas Water is the next village) is a real Cornish pub in a real Cornish village. The experienced leaseholders are David and Amanda Rowe, a local couple who previously ran the

They offer four or five real ales from the St Austell Brewery, and the food served in the separate restaurant is all sourced locally. Home-made pies are a speciality, and booking is recommended at the weekend, especially for the traditional Sunday lunch.

This relaxing meal can easily evolve into Sunday evening, when all are welcome to join in the weekly quiz. The inn's façade has an attractive covering of creeper, and the front patio is adorned with flowers in tubs and troughs. has access for people with disabilities.

35 Llawnroc Inn

Chute Lane, Gorran Haven, Cornwall PL26 6NU
☎ 01726 843461
🌐 www.llawnroc.mevagissey.com

Real Ales, Bar Food, Restaurant Menu, Accommodation, No Smoking Area, Disabled Facilities

- ☛ 7 miles south of St Austell off the B3273
- 🍺 Sharp's Doom Bar, Llawnroc own brew, guests
- 🍴 Lunch and dinner in bar or restaurant
- 🛏 8 en suite sea-facing rooms
- 🚗 Garden, patio, car park
- 💳 Major cards
- 🕐 12-11 (Sun to 10.30)
- 🏛 South West Coast Path; Mevagissey 2 miles, Lost Gardens of Heligan 3 miles, St Austell 7 miles

Llawnroc Inn is a friendly village pub overlooking the picturesque village and the sheltered bay of Gorran Haven, right on the South West Coast Path. On the ground floor are a locals bar (with a log fire in winter), a

lounge bar and a non-smoking dining area.

A good selection of cask ales, draught and bottle beers, lagers, wines and spirits is available, and the menus, ranging from snacks and buffets to a full à la carte, features locally caught fish and shellfish and meat from a top-class local butcher. There are fine views from the leafy garden and from the eight attractive bedrooms, all with en suite facilities and central heating.

Guests arriving by train can be collected from St Austell or Newquay station. The pub's curious name seems more familiar when read backwards!

31 Kings Arms

17 Fore Street, Mevagissey, St Austell,
Cornwall PL26 6UQ Tel: 01726 843869

Real Ales

32 Kings Arms

6 Fore Street, St Stephen, St Austell,
Cornwall PL26 7NN
Tel: 01726 822408

Real Ales, Disabled Facilities

33 Kings Arms

Bridges, Luxulyan, St Austell, Cornwall PL30 5EF
Tel: 01726 850202

Real Ales, Bar Food

34 Kings Arms

Tregony, Cornwall TR2 5RN
Tel: 01872 530202

Real Ales, Bar Food, Restaurant Menu,
No Smoking Area, Disabled Facilities

35 **Llawnroc Inn**

Gorran Haven, St Austell, Cornwall PL26 6NU
Tel: 01726 843461

Real Ales, Bar Food, Restaurant Menu,
Accommodation, No Smoking Area, Disabled Facilities

See panel opposite

36 Lostwithiel Hotel Golf and Country Club

Lower Polscoe, Lostwithiel, Cornwall PL22 0HQ
Tel: 01208 873550

Real Ales, Bar Food, Restaurant Menu,
Accommodation, No Smoking Area, Disabled Facilities

37 Luggar Inn

The Quay, Polruan, Cornwall PL23 1PA
Tel: 01726 870007

Real Ales, Bar Food, Restaurant Menu,
Accommodation, No Smoking Area

38 Lugger Inn

Fore Street, Fowey, Cornwall PL23 1AH
Tel: 01726 833435

Real Ales, Bar Food, Restaurant Menu,
No Smoking Area

39 New Inn

Fore Street, Tywardreath, Par, Cornwall PL24 2QP
Tel: 01726 813901

Real Ales, Bar Food, Restaurant Menu,
Accommodation, No Smoking Area, Disabled Facilities

40 **Noughts and Crosses**

Lansallos St, Polperro, Looe, Cornwall PL13 2QU
Tel: 01503 272239

Real Ales, Bar Food, Restaurant Menu,
No Smoking Area

See panel on page 78

41 O'Callaghan's

3 Market Street, St Austell, Cornwall PL25 4BB
Tel: 01726 76399

Real Ales, Bar Food

42 Old Ferry Inn

Bodinnick, Fowey, Cornwall PL23 1LX
Tel: 01726 870237

Real Ales, Bar Food, Restaurant Menu,
Accommodation, No Smoking Area, Disabled Facilities

43 Old Mill House

Mill Hill, Polperro, Cornwall PL13 2RP
Tel: 01503 272362

Real Ales, Bar Food, Restaurant Menu,
Accommodation, No Smoking Area, Disabled Facilities

44 Pack Horse Inn

Fore Street, St Blazey, Par, Cornwall PL24 2NH
Tel: 01726 813970

Real Ales, Bar Food, Restaurant Menu,
No Smoking Area, Disabled Facilities

45 Par Inn

2 Harbour Road, Par, Cornwall PL24 2BD
Tel: 01726 813961

Real Ales, Bar Food, Restaurant Menu,
No Smoking Area, Disabled Facilities

46 Peir House Hotel

Harbour Front, Charlestown, St Austell,
Cornwall PL25 3NJ Tel: 01726 67955

Real Ales, Bar Food, Restaurant Menu,
Accommodation, No Smoking Area

40 Noughts & Crosses

Lansallos Street, Polperro, Cornwall PL13 2QU
☎ 01503 272239

Real Ales, Bar Food, Restaurant Menu,
No Smoking Area

- ☞ 5 miles west of Looe
- 🍺 Sharp's Doom Bar + 3 guest ales, Scrumpy Jack, Guiness Extra Cold, Carling, Carlsberg Export, Fosters Super Chilled, Strongbow, John Smiths
- ❚ Homemade dishes, steak and seafood specialities
- 🎵 Live music Saturday in season, monthly out of season
- 💳 Major cards and cash machine
- 🕐 11-11
- 🏛 South West Coast Path; Looe 4 miles, Fowey 6 miles

Noughts & Crosses is a pub of real character, on three levels by the side of the river that runs down the village to the harbour. Visitors have a choice of bars and restaurants (including a non-smoking family room on the first floor) in which to sample the excellent choice of real ales (Sharp's Doom Bar and several guest ales) and a good selection of wine to enjoy by the glass or to accompany a fine selection of food. Hosts David and Vicky set great store by local produce, including freshly landed fish and shellfish and meat from a top local butcher. The Sunday roasts are always very popular in the winter time and other favourites include dressed crab, homemade dishes such as fish pie, steak & guiness pie and steak specialities. Children and dogs welcome.

51 The Punch Bowl Inn

Lanreath, nr Looe, Cornwall PL13 2NX
☎ 01503 220218

Real Ales, Bar Food, Restaurant Menu,
Accommodation, No Smoking Area

- ☞ Half a mile off the B3359 between the A390 and the A387 coastal road
- 🍺 Sharps + guests
- ❚ 12-2.30 & 6-9
- 🛏 10 en suite rooms
- 🅿 Car park
- 💳 Major cards accepted
- 🕐 L & D; all day Fri, Sat & Sun
- 🏛 Lanreath Folk & Farm Museum 1 mile, Looe 5 miles, Liskeard 7 miles

The Punch Bowl Inn stands on a bend in the pretty village of Lanreath, halfway between the A390 and A387. The oldest part of the premises date from the 13th century, and the whole place is full of character, with thick walls, flagstone floors, beams, panelling and an interesting mixture of chairs and tables. This is very much a family affair, with a local couple Chris and Trudi Hocking assisted by Sophie, Sam, Baz and Saskia. The local Sharps Brewery provides one of the three real ales always available, and most of the family joins in the preparation of the dishes that make up the printed menu and the extensive specials board. The area around the Punch Bowl has plenty to attract the visitor, and the inn has 10 en suite guest bedrooms open throughout the year. Children are very welcome at the inn.

47 Penryn House Hotel

The Coombes, Polperro, Looe, Cornwall PL13 2RQ
Tel: 01503 272157

Restaurant Menu, Accommodation, No Smoking Area,
Disabled Facilities

48 Poachers Inn

23 Fore Street, Roche, Cornwall PL26 8EP
Tel: 01726 890200

Real Ales, Bar Food, Restaurant Menu,
Disabled Facilities

49 The Polgooth Inn

Ricketts Lane, Polgooth, St Austell,
Cornwall PL26 7DA
Tel: 01726 74089

Real Ales, Bar Food, No Smoking Area,
Disabled Facilities

50 Porth Avallen Hotel

Sea Road, Carlyon Bay, St Austell,
Cornwall PL25 3SG
Tel: 01726 812802

Real Ales, Bar Food, Restaurant Menu,
Accommodation, No Smoking Area, Disabled Facilities

51 The Punch Bowl Inn

Lanreath, Looe, Cornwall PL13 2NX
Tel: 01503 220218

Real Ales, Bar Food, Restaurant Menu,
Accommodation, No Smoking Area

See panel opposite

52 Queens Head

1 The Square, St Austell, Cornwall PL26 7NH
Tel: 01726 822407

Real Ales, Bar Food, Restaurant Menu,
Accommodation, Disabled Facilities

53 Rashleigh Inn

Polkerris, Par, Cornwall PL24 2TL
Tel: 01726 813991

Real Ales, Bar Food, Restaurant Menu,
No Smoking Area, Disabled Facilities

54 Restormel Lodge Hotel

7 Castle Hill, Lostwithiel, Cornwall PL22 0DD
Tel: 01208 872223

Real Ales, Bar Food, Restaurant Menu,
Accommodation, No Smoking Area, Disabled Facilities

55 Rising Sun Inn

Portmellon Cove, Mevagissey, St Austell,
Cornwall PL26 6PL
Tel: 01726 843235

Real Ales, Bar Food, Restaurant Menu,
Accommodation, No Smoking Area, Disabled Facilities

56 Rock Inn

Roche, St Austell, Cornwall PL26 8EP
Tel: 01726 890710

Real Ales, Bar Food, Restaurant Menu,
No Smoking Area, Disabled Facilities

57 Royal Inn

66 Eastcliffe Road, Par, Cornwall PL24 2AJ
Tel: 01726 815601

Real Ales, Bar Food, Restaurant Menu,
Accommodation, No Smoking Area, Disabled Facilities

See panel on page 80

58 Royal Oak

Duke Street, Lostwithiel, Cornwall PL22 0AH
Tel: 01208 872552

Real Ales, Bar Food, Restaurant Menu,
Accommodation, No Smoking Area, Disabled Facilities

See panel on page 80

59 Royal Talbot Hotel

Duke Street, Lostwithiel, Cornwall PL22 0AG
Tel: 01208 872498

Real Ales, Bar Food, Restaurant Menu,
Accommodation, No Smoking Area, Disabled Facilities

60 Russell Inn

West Street , Polruan, Cornwall PL23 1PJ
Tel: 01726 870292

Real Ales, Bar Food, Restaurant Menu,
No Smoking Area, Disabled Facilities

57 The Royal Inn

Eastcliffe Road, Par, nr Fowey, Cornwall PL24 2AJ
☎ 01726 815601 🌐 www.royal-inn.co.uk

Real Ales, Bar Food, Restaurant Menu, Accommodation, No Smoking Area, Disabled Facilities

- On the A3082 2 miles east of St Austell
- Sharp's, Skinner's, guests
- Seasonally changing lunch and dinner menus
- 17 rooms (2 four-posters; 1 with disabled facilities)
- Quiz Wednesday; live music 2 Saturdays per month
- Patio
- Major cards
- CAMRA listed
- No pets in bedrooms
- 11.30-11 (Sun to 10.30)
- St Austell bay and beaches 3 miles, St Catherine's Castle 3 miles, Eden Project 2 miles

The **Royal Inn** at Par is only four miles from the Eden Project and is the perfect base for exploring this world-renowned site and the many other attractions of the region. Superb en suite accommodation includes double and twin rooms and a room specially adapted for disabled visitors. All the rooms have full-size baths with showers above, sofas or twin easy chairs, television and tea/coffee making facilities. The bright conservatory restaurant is a lovely sunlit area with Cornish slate flooring and attractive French oak tables and chairs. The finest and freshest seasonal produce is used on seasonally changing menus that cater in fine style for all tastes. This popular, welcoming inn is CAMRA recommended for its excellent real ales.

58 The Royal Oak

Duke Street, Lostwithiel, Cornwall PL22 0AH
☎ 01208 872552

Real Ales, Bar Food, Restaurant Menu, Accommodation, No Smoking Area, Disabled Facilities

- In Lostwithiel just yards off the A390
- Doom Bar, London Pride, Bass
- 12-2 & 6.30-9/9.30
- 6 rooms (5 en suite)
- Garden, car park
- Major cards except Amex and Diners
- 11-11 (Sun 12-10.30)
- Restormel Castle 1 mile, Lerryn 2 miles, Lanhydrock 4 miles, Bodmin 6 miles, Fowey 6 miles

The **Royal Oak** is a 13th century inn with a fine reputation for hospitality, food, drink and accommodation. Steve Pitt and Jo Lado, both talented and experienced chefs, took over as leaseholders in the summer of 2005, and took no time in making their mark at this very special free house. Up to half a dozen real ales are written on a chalkboard in the atmospheric bar, where another board lists the daily specials that supplement the printed menu. The fish dishes and steaks are particular favourites, but everything is very fresh and very good. The Royal Oak, easily reached from the A38 or A390, is an ideal base for a break in a delightful part of the county. Lostwithiel itself is full of interest, and local attractions include Restormel Castle, the National Trust's spectacular Lanhydrock House and the lovely old seafaring town of Fowey. The six bedrooms are available all year round.

61 Safe Harbour Hotel

Lostwithiel Street, Fowey, Cornwall PL23 1BQ
Tel: 01726 833379

Real Ales, Bar Food, Restaurant Menu,
Accommodation, No Smoking Area

62 Sawles Arms

Carthew, Nr St Austell, Cornwall PL26 8XH
Tel: 01726 850317

Real Ales, Bar Food

63 Seven Stars Inn

1 East Hill, St Austell, Cornwall PL25 4TW
Tel: 01726 72648

Real Ales, Bar Food

64 Ship Hotel

Fore Street, Mevagissey, St Austell,
Cornwall PL26 6UQ
Tel: 01726 843324

Real Ales, Bar Food, Restaurant Menu,
Accommodation, No Smoking Area, Disabled Facilities

65 Ship Inn

Fore Street, Polperro, Looe, Cornwall PL13 2QR
Tel: 01503 272453

Real Ales, Bar Food, No Smoking Area

66 The Ship Inn

Fore Street, Lerryn, Lostwithiel,
Cornwall PL22 0PT
Tel: 01208 872374

Real Ales, Bar Food, Restaurant Menu,
Accommodation, No Smoking Area, Disabled Facilities

See panel below

67 Ship Inn

Trafalgar Square, Fowey, Cornwall PL23 1AZ
Tel: 01726 832230

Real Ales, Bar Food, Restaurant Menu,
Accommodation, No Smoking Area

See panel on page 82

66 The Ship Inn

Lerryn, nr Lostwithiel, Cornwall PL22 0PT

☎ 01208 872374

⊕ www.cornwall-online.co.uk/shipinn-lerryn/

Real Ales, Bar Food, Restaurant Menu, Accommodation, No Smoking Area, Disabled Facilities

☛ 2 miles south of Lostwithiel on a minor road
off the A390

🍺 Selection of traditional ales

🍴 Daytime snacks, full evening menu

🛏 5 en suite rooms

⚓ Garden, own boat

💳 Mastercard, Visa

🕐 11-2.30 & 6-11

🏛 Lostwithiel 2 miles, Fowey 4 miles, Restormel
Castle 3 miles, Eden Project 8 miles

Cornwall is a land of creeks, and none is more beautiful than the one on which sits the picturesque village of Lerryn, close to the River Fowey. In the centre of this unspoilt village stands The Ship Inn, a fine old hostelry that dates back at least to the 17th century.

The interior has a splendidly authentic and traditional look, and the bar and lounge provide a delightful ambience in which to enjoy a glass of cask ale; when the sun shines, the garden overlooking the creek comes into its own. In the conservatory-style restaurant Cornish produce is king on the appealing, regularly changing menu. The Ship is an ideal choice for a Cornish holiday, and the inn's five en suite guest bedrooms are particularly comfortable and spacious. Walking, riding and fishing (the inn has its own boat) are popular activities, and the beach is close by.

67 The Ship Inn

Trafalgar Square, Fowey, Cornwall PL23 1AZ
☎ 01726 832230

Real Ales, Bar Food, Restaurant Menu, Accommodation, No Smoking Area

☞ On a corner site on Fowey's main thoroughfare

🍺 HSD, St Austell's Tribute and Tinners

🍴 12-9.30 (winter 12-2.15 & 6.30-9)

🛏 Variety of rooms from basic doubles to family suites and a four-poster

💳 Major cards accepted

🕐 11-11 (Sun 12-10.30)

🏛 All the sights of Fowey

On a corner site on Fowey's main thoroughfare, the whitewashed Ship Inn has a long and distinguished history going back almost 500 years. The whole place has a lovely

traditional appeal, with wooden floors, beamed ceilings and a cosy, atmospheric bar where HSD, Tribute and Tinners from the St Austell real ales head a full range of beers, lagers, ciders, wines, spirits and soft drinks.

The connection with the sea and ships goes far beyond the inn's name, and among many pictures and memorabilia with a nautical theme the highlight of the décor is a superb stained-glass window in the restaurant depicting the ships of Fowey preparing to meet the Spanish Armada. The inn is open all day, every day, for drinks, and food is also served throughout the day and well into the evening in summer, and lunchtime and evening in winter. It is appropriate that locally caught fish and shellfish are the specialities on the menu, but meat-eaters and vegetarians are also well catered for. This is one of the best and most popular eating places in the region, and booking is strongly advised at the weekend.

Tenants Dougie and Justine are excellent hosts, and as well as providing outstanding food and drink they also offer accommodation in a variety of bedrooms to suit all needs. These comprise three basic double rooms, a twin room, an en suite double room plus single bed, a splendid oak-panelled room with a handsome oak four-poster, and a family suite for up to six guests. The lovely old port of Fowey (pronounced Foy) is well worth taking time to explore, with its steep, narrow streets that lead down to one of the finest natural harbours on the south coast. Dougie and Justine are ready to welcome all comers to the Ship, whether it's for a quick drink, a snack or a full meal, or to enjoy a relaxing break.

68 Ship Inn

Polmear Hill, Par, Cornwall PL24 2AR
Tel: 01726 812540

Real Ales, Bar Food, Restaurant Menu,
Accommodation, No Smoking Area, Disabled Facilities

69 Ship Inn

West End, Pentewan, St Austell,
Cornwall PL26 6BX
Tel: 01726 842855

Real Ales, Bar Food, Restaurant Menu,
Accommodation, No Smoking Area

70 The Ship Inn

Portloe, Truro, Cornwall TR2 5RA
Tel: 01872 501356

Real Ales, Bar Food, Restaurant Menu,
Accommodation, No Smoking Area, Disabled Facilities

See panel below

70 The Ship Inn

Portloe, Cornwall TR2 5RA
☎ 01872 501356

**Real Ales, Bar Food, Restaurant Menu, Accommo-
dation, No Smoking Area, Disabled Facilities**

- ☛ Take the A3078 off the St Austell-Truro road
  4 miles before Truro
- 🍺 St Austell Tribute and Tinners
- 🍴 L & D 7 days a week
- 🛏 2 en suite rooms
- ⚓ Garden opposite, small car park
- 💳 Major cards except Amex
- 🕐 11-3 & 6-11 (all day in summer)
- 🏛 Veryan 2 miles, Truro 7 miles, St Austell 10
  miles

Ben Jago and Amy Hayman, a go-ahead
young Cornish couple, have recently taken
the helm at the Ship Inn, which stands in the
picturesque fishing village of Portloe. Nautical
memorabilia adorn the walls of the bar, and
the kitchen specialises in fresh fish dishes based
on the day's local catch. The Ship is also a
pleasant base for overnight guests, with two
comfortable en suite bedrooms.

71 Talland Bay Hotel

Porthallow, Looe, Cornwall PL13 2JB
Tel: 01503 272667

Bar Food, Restaurant Menu, Accommodation,
No Smoking Area, Disabled Facilities

72 Three Pilchards Inn

Quay Road, Polperro, Looe, Cornwall PL13 2QZ
Tel: 01503 272233

Real Ales, Bar Food

73 Tremarne Hotel

Polkirt Hill, Mevagissey, St Austell,
Cornwall PL26 6UY
Tel: 01726 842213

Bar Food, Restaurant Menu, Accommodation,
No Smoking Area

74 Trewhiddle Inn

Pentewan Road, St Austell, Cornwall PL26 7AD
Tel: 01726 67013

Real Ales, Bar Food, Restaurant Menu,
No Smoking Area, Disabled Facilities

75 Victoria Inn and Lodge

Victoria, Roche, St Austell, Cornwall PL26 8LQ
Tel: 01726 890207

Real Ales, Bar Food, Restaurant Menu,
Accommodation, No Smoking Area, Disabled Facilities

76 Water Wheel Country Inn and Restaurant

Bodmin Road, Trethowel, St Austell,
Cornwall PL25 5RR
Tel: 01726 67435

Restaurant Menu, Accommodation, No Smoking Area

77 Western Inn

West Hill, St Austell, Cornwall PL25 5EY
Tel: 01726 72797

Real Ales, Bar Food, Disabled Facilities

78 Ye Old Plough Horse Inn

Duloe, Liskeard, Cornwall PL14 4PN
Tel: 01503 262050

Real Ales, Bar Food, Restaurant Menu,
No Smoking Area, Disabled Facilities

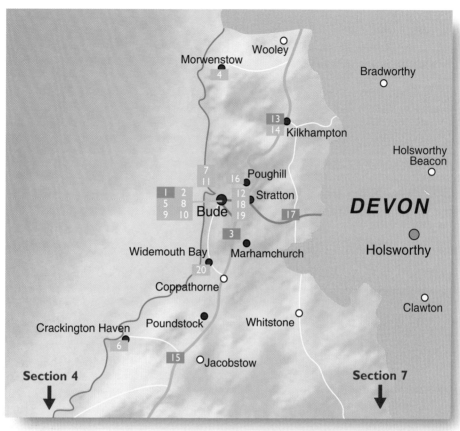

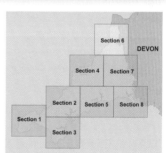

11	Pub or Inn Reference Number - Detailed Information
12	Pub or Inn Reference Number - Summary Entry
●■	Place of interest mentioned in the chapter introduction

NORTH CORNWALL

North Cornwall, like the rest of the county, has retained many Celtic traditions, notably in place names and in the ancient monuments that are to be found everywhere. Bude, the birthplace of British surfing, has long been a favourite holiday destination, and places of interest include the civil war stronghold of Stratton and the nearby site of the Battle of Stamford Hill.

Bude

A traditional seaside resort with three miles of sandy beaches, rock pools and Atlantic breakers that assisted its reputation as Britain's premier surfing venue. **Bude Canal** was an ambitious project intended to connect the Atlantic with the English Channel by way of the River Tamar. The stretch between Bude and Launceston was the only section to be completed, and is now a resource for leisure boating, fishing and walking. Close to the entrance to the canal stands **Bude Castle**, built and lived in by the 19th century engineer and inventor Sir Goldsworthy Gurney. The history of the town, the man and the canal is the theme of the **Bude-Stratton Museum**, housed in the Canal Company's former smithy. A recent attraction in Bude is **Bude Light 2000**, a 30ft beacon that uses advanced fibre optic techniques to represent the constellations at the time of the 2000 Millennium.

The Beach at Bude

Crackington Haven

One of the most dramatic places along this remarkable coast. The small cove is overlooked by towering cliffs and jagged rocks, and the setting was chosen for some episodes of the TV *Poldark* series. Just south of Crackington Haven a difficult path leads to a remote beach known as **The Strangles**, above which is High Cliff, the highest point on the Cornwall coast. On the coast road stands the National Trust's **Trevigue**, a working livestock farm and wildlife sanctuary.

Kilkhampton

Kilkhampton sits astride the A39 600 feet above sea level. Among the treasures in the 15th century **Church of St James** are monuments to the local Granville family, magnificent carved bench ends and an organ played by Purcell when it was in Westminster Abbey. **Brocklands Adventure Park** is one of the most popular family attractions in the vicinity.

Marhamchurch

This pleasant hilltop village was founded as a monastic settlement in the early 6th century, and the parish church is dedicated to the monastery's founder St Marwenne. An unusual feature is a 'sanctuary knocker' which allowed fugitives to seek 40 days' protection in the church.

Morwenstow

Morwenstow is an ideal place for observing the changing moods of the Atlantic, being located on the harshest stretch of the north Cornwall coast. The village's most renowned inhabitant was the eccentric vicar and poet Robert Stephen Hawker, who came here in 1834 and stayed among his congregation of 'smugglers, wreckers and dissenters' until his death in 1875 He assisted in the rescue of many shipwrecked sailors or the recovery of their bodies. One of the many ships wrecked off Sharpnose headland was the *Caledonia*, a Scottish ship whose figurehead stands above the grave of her captain in Morwenstow churchyard. Hawker spent much of his time in the driftwood hut he built near the clifftop: **Hawker's Hut** is in the care of the National Trust.

Poughill

The thatched cottages of the old village of Poughill stand round **St Olaf's Church**, where visitors can admire the 15th century carved bench ends and wall paintings of St Christopher.

Poundstock

Poundstock, which lies a short drive south of Bude off the A39, has an unusual **Guildhall** that was built in the 14th century, probably to house masons working on the parish church. The Atlantic is only a mile away, and the views from the cliffs stretch to Lundy Island in the north and Trevose Head in the south.

Stratton

This old market town was a stronghold of the Royalists during the Civil War, and their commander Sir Bevil Grenville made **The Tree Inn** his base of operations. In May 1643, at the Battle of Stamford hill, Grenville led his troops to victory over the Parliamentarians. The dead of both sides were buried in unmarked graves in Stratton churchyard. Grenville made an excellent choice for a bodyguard in the 7'4" shape of Anthony Payne, the Cornish Giant, who was born at The Tree Inn.

Widemouth Bay

Ever since the 1930s, this little village has been a popular holiday resort attracting visitors with its wide curving bay of flat sands. From Penhalt Cliff, at the southern end of Widemouth Sands, the view of the bay is breathtaking.

Widemouth Bay

1 The Bencoolen Inn

Bencoolen Road, Bude, Cornwall EX23 8PJ
Tel: 01288 354694

Real Ales, Bar Food, Restaurant Menu,
Accommodation, No Smoking Area

See panel below

2 Brendon Arms

Falcon Terrace, Bude, Cornwall EX23 8SD
Tel: 01288 354542

Real Ales, Bar Food, Restaurant Menu,
Accommodation, No Smoking Area, Disabled Facilities

3 Buller's Arms

Marhamchurch, Bude, Cornwall EX23 0HB
Tel: 01288 361277

Real Ales, Bar Food, Restaurant Menu,
Accommodation, No Smoking Area, Disabled Facilities

See panel on page 88

4 Bush Inn

Morwenstow, Cornwall EX23 9SR
Tel: 01288 331242

Real Ales, Bar Food, Restaurant Menu,
No Smoking Area, Disabled Facilities

5 Carriers Inn

The Strand, Bude, Cornwall EX23 8QU
Tel: 01288 352459

Real Ales, Bar Food, Restaurant Menu,
No Smoking Area, Disabled Facilities

6 Coombe Barton Inn

Crackington Haven, Nr Bude, Cornwall EX23 0JG
Tel: 01840 230345

Real Ales, Bar Food, Restaurant Menu,
Accommodation, No Smoking Area, Disabled Facilities

1 The Bencoolen Inn

Bencoolen Road, Bude, Cornwall EX23 8PJ
☎ 01288 354694

Real Ales, Bar Food, Restaurant Menu,
Accommodation, No Smoking Area

- ☛ Close to the town centre in Bude
- 3 to 4 local brews
- 12-4 & from 6
- Self-contained cottage
- Car park, garden
- All the major cards
- 12-11
- All the attractions of Bude

Built in 1862 as a private residence, the Bencoolen Inn has for many years been in the capable hands of Juan and Lorraine Puerta-Terron. The building was in a sorry state when they arrived, but with hard work and enthusiasm they have turned its fortunes round and built up a fine reputation for hospitality and fine cooking. The inn takes its name from a famous sailing ship, and pictures of this and other vessels can be seen in the public rooms. Four real ales from local breweries are served in the bar, where a substantial menu of popular dishes is available. But the main magnet for foodies is the intimate El Barco restaurant, where master-chef Juan presents an excellent menu of European and international cuisine.

3 Bullers Arms

Marhamchurch, nr Bude, Cornwall EX23 0HB
☎ 01288 361277 ⊕ www.bullersarms.co.uk

Real Ales, Bar Food, Restaurant Menu, Accommodation, No Smoking Area, Disabled Facilities

☞ Marhamchurch is off the A39 2 miles SE of Bude

🍺 Wide selection

🍴 12-2.30 & 6-9.30

🛏 11 en suite rooms

💳 Major cards except Diners

🕐 11-11 (Sun 12-10.30)

🏛 Bude 2 miles, Widemouth Bay 2 miles

The picturesque little village of Marhamchurch is best known for its beautiful church, but many of today's visitors come here to enjoy the outstanding amenities of the **Bullers Arms.**

Long known as one of the very best inns in North Cornwall, it became an inn in 1856, but the building itself dates back much further to the time when it was built as a typical Cornish 'long house'. Its name as an inn was initially the Kings Arms, but the name was changed after the Boer War to commemorate General Sir Redvers Buller, who relieved Ladysmith during the war and became a local hero – he was born just over the border in Devon. The origins and history of the inn give it a delightful feel of old-world charm, and a warm, welcoming ambience is generated by owners the Perry family – Tony, Yvonne and son Oliver.

The inside of the inn is a pure delight, with cosy corners, old stone and brick, polished dark wood, brass and framed period prints on the walls, and a wealth of knickknacks and memorabilia adding further colour and atmosphere. The bar at the Bullers Arms is well stocked with real ales and other beers, lagers, ciders, wines, spirits and soft drinks, and good honest food is served every lunchtime and evening. The chef and his staff insist on the very best and freshest seasonal produce, and the printed menu and daily specials board offer a choice for all tastes and appetites. The Sunday carvery is especially popular, but such is the reputation of the place that booking is recommended at any time.

The attractions of the Bullers Arms do not end at food and drink! It is also a perfect base for exploring an area that has a wealth of coastal and country delights to discover. The 11 keenly priced guest bedrooms are all decorated and furnished to a very high standard, and days begin with a choice of full English or lighter breakfasts.

7 Crooklets Inn

Crooklets Beach, Bude, Cornwall EX23 8NF
Tel: 01288 352335

Real Ales, Bar Food, Accommodation,
No Smoking Area

8 The Falcon Hotel

Breakwater Road, Bude, Cornwall EX23 8SD
Tel: 01288 352005

Real Ales, Bar Food, Restaurant Menu,
Accommodation, No Smoking Area, Disabled Facilities

9 Globe

13 The Strand, Bude, Cornwall EX23 8QU
Tel: 01288 352085

Real Ales, Bar Food, Restaurant Menu,
Accommodation, Disabled Facilities

10 Hartland Hotel

Hartland Terrace, Bude, Cornwall EX23 8JY
Tel: 01288 355661

Bar Food, Restaurant Menu, Accommodation,
No Smoking Area, Disabled Facilities

11 Inn On The Green

Crooklets Beach, Bude, Cornwall EX23 8NF
Tel: 01288 356013

Real Ales, Bar Food, Restaurant Menu,
Accommodation, No Smoking Area, Disabled Facilities

12 Kings Arms

Howells Road, Stratton, Bude, Cornwall EX23 9BX
Tel: 01288 352396

Real Ales, Bar Food, Accommodation,
No Smoking Area

13 The London Inn

Kilkhampton, Bude, Cornwall EX23 9QR
Tel: 01288 321665

Real Ales, Bar Food, Restaurant Menu,
Accommodation, No Smoking Area, Disabled Facilities

See panel below

14 The New Inn

Kilkhampton, Bude, Cornwall EX23 9QN
Tel: 01288 321488

Real Ales, Bar Food, Disabled Facilities

13 The London Inn

Kilkhampton, Cornwall EX23 9QR
☎ 01288 321665

Real Ales, Bar Food, Restaurant Menu, Accommodation, No Smoking Area, Disabled Facilities

- On the A39 4 miles N of Bude
- Sharps Doom Bar, Dartmoor
- 12-2 & 6.30-9
- Big TV screen for sports events
- Beer garden
- Major cards except Amex
- 11-3 & 6-11 (all day Wed, Fri, Sat & Sun)
- Brocklands Adventure Park, Bude 4 miles, Morweston 4 miles

The **London Inn** is a friendly pub in the village of Kilkhampton, which stands 600 feet above sea level by the A39 4 miles north of Bude. A local couple, Stewart and Lorraine Davey, have held the licence since 2002, and their first venture into the licensed trade has won them many friends. Sharps Doom Bar and Dartmoor are the regular real ales, heading a wide selection of drinks served in the bar, which features an eyecatching counter in tropical wood. Lorraine's cooking is a major factor in the success of the inn, and her delicious dishes are typified by lemon sole with a prawn and cheese sauce. The Sunday lunches are also highly recommended, and booking is advisable. Nearby Brocklands Adventure Park is one of the top family attractions in the region.

15 The Old Wainhouse Inn

Wainhouse Corner, St Gennys, nr Bude,
Cornwall EX23 0BA
☎ 01840 230711

**Real Ales, Bar Food, Restaurant Menu,
No Smoking Area, Disabled Facilities**

☛ By the main A39 at Wainhouse Corner, 8 miles S of Bude

🍺 Hicks, pub's own Old Wainhouse

🍴 11.30-2 & 5.30-9 (Sun 12-2 & 6.30-9)

⛽ Car park, beer garden

💳 Major cards except Amex

🕐 11-11

🏛 St Gennys 2 miles, Crackington Haven 2 miles, Marshgate 2 miles, Bude 8 miles

By the main A39 inland from St Gennys and Crackington Haven, the **Old Wainhouse Inn** is easy to spot with a painting of a coach and four on its façade. The inn's own Old Wainhouse brew heads a list of at least four real ales served in the bar, which features a flagstone floor, brasses, hops and lots of local memorabilia. The inn is rightly renowned for its food, and the printed menu and daily specials board are filled with good things to provide anything from a light snack to a three-course meal. Among the most popular choices are cod in a beer batter, grills and ham, egg & chips. The inn has a pleasant garden and a large off-road car park.

17 The Red Post Inn

Red Post, Launcells, nr Bude, Cornwall EX23 9NW
☎ 01288 381305 🌐 www.redpostinn.co.uk

Real Ales, Restaurant Menu, No Smoking Area

☛ Red Post lies 2½ miles east of Bude

🍺 Changing selection

🍴 6-9, also Sunday 12-3

🛏 Caravan park

⛽ Car park, garden

💳 Major cards except Amex

🕐 From 6, Sun from 12

🏛 St Swithin's Church Launcells 1 mile, Bude 2½ miles

Situated off the A3072 a couple of miles east of Bude, the **Red Post Inn** has been run since 2003 by Martin and Gill Sharp, their sons Dean and Paul and their daughter Natalie. Open every evening and Sunday lunchtime, the lovely old thatched inn is full of atmosphere and character.

The main part dates from 1531, but it is known that an inn stood on the site as far back as the 9th century, and down the ages the inn has played an important part in the area's history. A full range of drinks is served in the bar, and food is available every evening.

Natalie is the cook, and her printed menu and specials board provide an excellent choice that includes fresh fish and popular steaks and mixed grills.

15 Old Wainhouse Inn
Wainhouse Corner , St Gennys, Bude,
Cornwall EX23 0BA
Tel: 01840 230711

Real Ales, Bar Food, Restaurant Menu,
No Smoking Area, Disabled Facilities

See panel opposite

16 Preston Gate Inn
Poughill, Bude, Cornwall EX23 9ET
Tel: 01288 354017

Real Ales, Bar Food, No Smoking Area,
Disabled Facilities

17 The Red Post Inn
Launcells, Bude, Cornwall EX23 9NW
Tel: 01288 381305

Real Ales, Restaurant Menu, No Smoking Area

See panel opposite

18 Stratton Gardens Hotel
Cot Hill, Stratton, Bude, Cornwall EX23 9DN
Tel: 01288 352500

Real Ales, Bar Food, Restaurant Menu,
Accommodation, No Smoking Area

19 Tree Inn
Fore Street, Stratton, Cornwall EX23 9DA
Tel: 01288 352038

Real Ales, Bar Food, Restaurant Menu,
Accommodation, No Smoking Area, Disabled Facilities

20 Widemouth Manor Hotel
Widemouth Bay, Bude, Cornwall EX23 0DE
Tel: 01288 361263

Real Ales, Bar Food, Restaurant Menu,
Accommodation, No Smoking Area

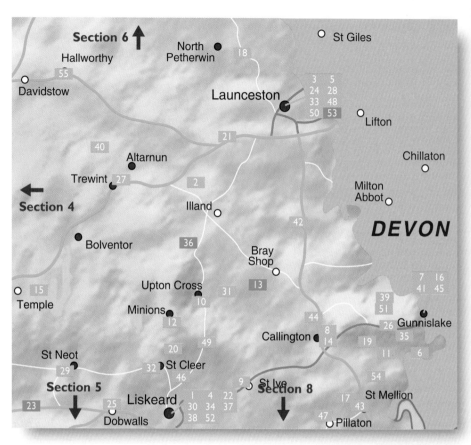

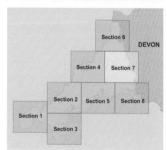

11	Pub or Inn Reference Number - Detailed Information
12	Pub or Inn Reference Number - Summary Entry
● ■	Place of interest mentioned in the chapter introduction

CENTRAL CORNWALL

Bodmin Moor is rich in tales of mystery and romance, none more than the much visited Jamaica Inn, the inspiration of Daphne du Maurier's famous novel. On the edge of the moor, Launceston was a great favourite of Sir John Betjeman, and Liskeard - one of the five stannary towns – is still rich in tin mining heritage. The mining legacy is strong throughout the area and the Minions Heritage Centre includes the story of mining and miners, as well as the life and times of much earlier inhabitants.

Altarnum

The splendid 15th century parish church, often referred to as the 'Cathedral of the Moors', is dedicated to St Nonna, mother of St David of Wales. In the churchyard stands the only relic of St Nonna's time, a Celtic cross thought to date from a round AD527, when St Nonna came here from Wales.

Bolventor

At the heart of Bodmin Moor, Bolventor is the location of the coaching inn immortalised in Daphne du Maurier's novel *Jamaica Inn*. One room is filled with du Maurier memorabilia, and another houses a museum of curiosities collected by a Victorian taxidermist. To the south lies the mysterious **Dozmary Pool**, where legend has it that the Lady of the Lake received King Arthur's sword Excalibur.

Callington

There's plenty to interest the visitor in this old market town at the foot of Kit Hill. The area's heritage, character and landscape can be seen by wandering round the town and

Altarnum Church

discovering the **Mural Project**, a series of local scenes painted on the walls of the town's buildings. Callington is the headquarters of the well-known pasty-makers Ginsters.

Gunnislake

Often referred to as 'the first village in Cornwall', Gunnislake is set in the beautiful Tamar valley. The striking **New Bridge**, a seven-arched granite structure, is one of the major gateways into the county.

Launceston

On the eastern edge of Bodmin Moor and close to the border with Devon, Launceston was a great favourite of Sir John Betjeman, who called it 'the most interesting town in inland Cornwall'. Dating originally from Celtic times, it was until 1838 the county capital. There's plenty for the visitor to discover, including a ruined castle, two fine churches and the **Lawrence House Museum**. To the west of town, the **Launceston Steam Railway** takes passengers on a narrow-gauge run through the beautiful Kensey Valley.

Liskeard

One of Cornwall's five famous stannary towns — the others are Bodmin, Lostwithiel, Truro and Helston. The history of tin mining is one of the topics covered in the fascinating

Liskeard & District Museum, which was opened by HRH Prince Charles in June 2002. The **Church of St Martin** is the second largest parish church in the county.

Minions

Minions was once a thriving mining centre, and that legacy is explained in the **Minions Heritage Centre**. Close to the village stand **Hurlers Stone Circle** – a Bronze Age temple comprising three circles – and the **Cheesewring**, a pile of granite slabs caused by natural erosion and glaciation.

North Petherwin

Situated above the River Ottery, this village is home to the **Tamar Otter Sanctuary**, a branch of the famous Otter Trust that's dedicated to breeding otters for release into the wild to save the species from extinction in lowland England.

St Cleer

A sizable Moorland village in the heart of former mining country, St Cleer is set

Launceston Castle

around its 15th century parish church. Close by is a Holy Well, one of a number of preserved wells in the county. One mile east of the village stands **Trevethy Quoit**, an impressive chamber tomb believed to be more than 5,000 years old.

St Neot

The **Church of St Anietus** boasts some wonderful 16th century stained glass and a fine granite cross dating from the 9th century. One window depicts St Neot, who became famous for miracles associated with animals. Just south of the village are the **Carnglaze Slate Caverns**, three vast underground caverns created by local slate miners. Also here is an amazing subterranean lake.

Trewint

John Wesley, the founder of the Methodist Church, was a frequent visitor to Trewint, and in **Wesley Cottage** the rooms he used have been maintained in the style of his day.

Upton Cross

This handsome village is the home of **Cornish Yarg Cheese**, made since 1983. Visitors can watch the cheesemaking process and the milking of the dairy herd, and follow pond and woodland trails.

1 The Albion

Dean St, Liskeard, Cornwall PL14 4AA
Tel: 01579 342643

Real Ales

2 The Archer Arms

Lewannick, Launceston, Cornwall PL15 7QD
Tel: 01566 782450

Real Ales, Bar Food, Restaurant Menu,
No Smoking Area, Disabled Facilities

3 Bakers Arms

Southgate Street, Launceston, Cornwall PL15 9DP
Tel: 01566 772510

Real Ales, Accommodation

4 Barley Sheaf

Church Street, Liskeard, Cornwall PL14 3AQ
Tel: 01579 342055

Real Ales

5 Bell Inn

1 Tower St, Launceston, Cornwall PL15 8BQ
Tel: 01566 775154

Real Ales

6 The Boot Inn

Fore St, Calstock, Cornwall PL18 9RN
Tel: 01822 834866

Real Ales, Restaurant Menu, No Smoking Area

7 The Buccaneer Inn

Commercial Street, Gunnislake,
Cornwall PL18 9JW
Tel: 01822 833752

Real Ales

8 Bulls Head Hotel

Fore Street, Callington, Cornwall PL17 7AD
Tel: 01579 383387

Real Ales

9 Butchers Arms

St Ive, Liskeard, Cornwall PL14 3LX
Tel: 01579 382298

Real Ales, Bar Food, Restaurant Menu,
No Smoking Area, Disabled Facilities

10 Caradon Inn

Upton Cross, Liskeard, Cornwall PL14 5AZ
Tel: 01579 362391

Real Ales, Bar Food, Restaurant Menu,
Accommodation, No Smoking Area, Disabled Facilities

11 Carpenters Arms

Lower Metherell, Callington, Cornwall PL17 8BJ
Tel: 01579 350242

Real Ales, Bar Food, Restaurant Menu,
Accommodation, No Smoking Area

12 Cheesewring Hotel

Minions, Nr Liskeard, Cornwall PL14 5LE
Tel: 01579 362321

Real Ales, Bar Food, Restaurant Menu,
Accommodation, No Smoking Area, Disabled Facilities

13 Church House Inn

Linkinhorne, nr Callington, Cornwall PL17 7LY
☎ 01579 363631

Real Ales, Bar Food, Restaurant Menu,
No Smoking Area, Disabled Facilities

☛ Linkinhorne lies off the A388 about 4 miles north of Callington

🍺 Sharp's Doom Bar, Skinner's Knocker

🍴 Home-cooked dishes on bar and à la carte menus

♫ Skittle alley

⛏ Car park

💳 All the major cards

🏆 Former nominated Community Pub of the Year

🕐 7-11 Tue-Sun, 12-3 Sat & Sun

🏛 Callington 4 miles, Kit Hill 4 miles, Upton Cross 3 miles, Minions 5 miles

Church House Inn is a convivial family-run village pub offering a pleasant mix of plush and rustic in its bar and non-smoking restaurant. It stands in great walking country, and it caters for fresh-air thirsts and appetites with real ales from local breweries and excellent home cooking featuring super steaks and fish dishes.

13 Church House Inn

Linkinhorne, Callington, Cornwall PL17 7LY
Tel: 01579 363631

Real Ales, Bar Food, Restaurant Menu,
No Smoking Area, Disabled Facilities

See panel opposite

14 Coachmakers Arms

Newport Square, Callington, Cornwall PL17 7AS
Tel: 01579 382567

Real Ales, Bar Food, Restaurant Menu,
Accommodation, No Smoking Area, Disabled Facilities

15 Colliford Tavern

St Neot, Liskeard, Cornwall PL14 6PZ
Tel: 01208 821335

Real Ales, Bar Food, Restaurant Menu,
Accommodation, No Smoking Area, Disabled Facilities

16 Cornish Inn

The Square, Fore Street, Gunnislake,
Cornwall PL18 9BW
Tel: 01822 834040

Real Ales, Bar Food, Accommodation

17 Coryton Arms

St Mellion, Saltash, Cornwall PL12 6RJ
Tel: 01579 350322

Real Ales, Bar Food

18 The Countryman

Langdon Cross, North Petherwin, Launceston,
Cornwall PL15 8NJ
Tel: 01566 785333

Real Ales, Bar Food, Restaurant Menu,
Accommodation, No Smoking Area, Disabled Facilities

19 Cross House Inn

Metherell, Callington, Cornwall PL17 8BQ
Tel: 01579 350482

Real Ales, Bar Food, Restaurant Menu,
Accommodation, No Smoking Area, Disabled Facilities

20 Crows Nest Inn

Crows Nest, Liskeard, Cornwall PL14 5JG
Tel: 01579 345930

Real Ales, Bar Food, Restaurant Menu,
No Smoking Area, Disabled Facilities

23 Halfway House Inn

Twowatersfoot, nr Trago Mills, Liskeard,
Cornwall PL14 6HR
☎ 01208 821242/821115

Real Ales, Bar Food, Restaurant Menu,
No Smoking Area, Disabled Facilities

☛ The inn stands on the A38 between Trago
Mills and Bodmin Road station.

🍺 Cornish Breweries featured

🍴 A la carte menus (all day in summer, L & D in
winter)

⛄ Car park, beer garden

🚫 Not Amex

🕐 11-11

🏛 Bodmin Moor 2 miles, Dobwalls Adventure
Park 2 miles, Lanhydrock House 3 miles,
Bodmin 6 miles, Liskeard 6 miles

Quality, hospitality and service are
watchwords at the Halfway House Inn,
which is located in the tranquil village of
Twowatersfoot where the Fowey and Neot
rivers meet.

Open all day, every day, this mid-Victorian
coaching inn enjoys a superb setting close to a
steep forested valley on the edge of Bodmin
Moor, halfway between Liskeard and Bodmin
(hence the name).

Cornish breweries are featured among the
real ales, and in the non-smoking dining area
proprietor Ceri Marshall and her staff prepare
a full menu that satisfies for all tastes and
appetites – special dietary needs can be
catered for with a little notice. The garden and
grounds provide lovely views and gentle strolls
along the riverbank.

21 The Eliot Arms

Launceston, Cornwall PL15 7EU
Tel: 01566 772051

Real Ales, Bar Food, Restaurant Menu,
No Smoking Area, Disabled Facilities

22 The Fountain

3 The Parade, Liskeard, Cornwall PL14 6AH
Tel: 01579 342154

Real Ales, Bar Food, Disabled Facilities

23 Halfway House Inn

Twowatersfoot, Liskeard, Cornwall PL14 6HR
Tel: 01208 821242

Real Ales, Bar Food, Restaurant Menu,
No Smoking Area, Disabled Facilities

See panel on page 97

24 Harvey's

13 Church Street, Launceston,
Cornwall PL15 8AW
Tel: 01566 772558

Real Ales, Bar Food, Restaurant Menu,
No Smoking Area

25 The Highwayman

Dobwalls, Cornwall PL14 6JG
Tel: 01579 320114

Real Ales, Bar Food

26 The Hingston Inn

StAnns Chapel, Gunnislake, Cornwall PL18 9NB
Tel: 01822 832468

Bar Food

1262 The Racehorse Inn

North Hill, nr Launceston, Cornwall PL15 7PG
☎ 01566 786916
🌐 robbie@theracehorseinn-
cornwall.wanadoo.co.uk
Proprietors: Robbie & Pat Cox

Real Ales, Bar Food, Restaurant Menu,
Accommodation

☛ From Launceston (A30) take the B3257 then B3254

🍺 Sharps Doom Bar

🍴 Comprehensive menu, daily specials, Sunday roast

🛏 3 en suite double rooms

🚗 Car park, decking, beer garden

💳 The major cards

🕐 12-3 & 6.30-11

🏛 Kilmar Tor 1 mile, Minions 3 miles, Upton Cross 4 miles

Standing off the B3254 on the eastern edge of Bodmin Moor, The Racehorse Inn is a delightful free house that started life as the village school. Coal fires warm the two beamed bars, which feature horseracing memorabilia, including a handsome copper relief of a racehorse and winning post above the hearth; when the sun shines visitors can enjoy the grand country views from the garden. The local brewery Sharp's heads the real ales, locally sourced well-priced quality food is served in the bar and restaurant – the non-smoking section at the rear overlooks the patio. The area around The Racehorse is rich in scenic and historic interest, and the inn's three en suite bedrooms provide a perfect base for a walking or touring holiday.

27 Kings Head Hotel

Five Lanes ,Altarnun, Launceston,
Cornwall PL15 7RX
Tel: 01566 86241

Real Ales, Bar Food, Restaurant Menu,
Accommodation, No Smoking Area, Disabled Facilities

28 Launceston Arms

Exeter Street, Launceston, Cornwall PL15 9EQ
Tel: 01566 779080

Real Ales

29 London Inn

St Neot, Liskeard, Cornwall PL14 6NG
Tel: 01579 320263

Real Ales, Bar Food, Restaurant Menu,
No Smoking Area, Disabled Facilities

30 The Lord Elliot Hotel

Castle Street, Liskeard, Cornwall PL14 3AU
Tel: 01579 342717

Bar Food, Restaurant Menu, Accommodation,
No Smoking Area, Disabled Facilities

31 Manor House Inn and Restaurant

Rilla Mill, Callington, Cornwall PL17 7NT
Tel: 01579 362354

Real Ales, Bar Food, Restaurant Menu,
No Smoking Area, Disabled Facilities

32 Market Inn

Well Lane, St Cleer, Liskeard, Cornwall PL14 5DG
Tel: 01579 342091

Real Ales, Bar Food, Restaurant Menu,
No Smoking Area, Disabled Facilities

33 Newmarket Inn

1 Race Hill, Launceston, Cornwall PL15 9BA
Tel: 01566 774246

Real Ales, Bar Food, Restaurant Menu,
Accommodation, No Smoking Area, Disabled Facilities

34 Old Stag

Station Road, Liskeard, Cornwall PL14 4DA
Tel: 01579 342280

Real Ales, Bar Food, Restaurant Menu,
No Smoking Area

35 Queens Head

Albaston, Gunnislake, Cornwall PL18 9AJ
Tel: 01822 832482

Real Ales, Bar Food

36 The Racehorse Inn

North Hill, Launceston, Cornwall PL15 7PG
Tel: 01566 786916

Real Ales, Bar Food, Restaurant Menu,
Accommodation

See panel opposite

37 The Railway Hotel

6 Barn Street, Liskeard, Cornwall PL14 4BJ
Tel: 01579 342656

Real Ales

38 Red Lion

5 Lower Lux St, Liskeard, Cornwall PL14 3JL
Tel: 01579 347837

39 Rifle Volunteer Inn

St Anns Chapel, Tamar Valley, Cornwall PL18 9HL
Tel: 01822 832508

Real Ales, Bar Food, Restaurant Menu,
Accommodation, No Smoking Area

40 The Rising Sun

Altarnun, Nr Launceston, Cornwall PL15 7SN
Tel: 01566 86636

Real Ales, Bar Food, Restaurant Menu,
Accommodation, No Smoking Area, Disabled Facilities

41 Rising Sun Inn

Calstock Road, Gunnislake, Cornwall PL18 9BX
Tel: 01822 832201

Real Ales, Bar Food, Restaurant Menu,
No Smoking Area, Disabled Facilities

42 Springer Spaniel

Treburley, Launceston, Cornwall PL15 9NS
Tel: 01579 370424

Real Ales, Bar Food, Restaurant Menu,
Accommodation, No Smoking Area, Disabled Facilities

43 St Mellion International Hotel

St Mellion, Saltash, Cornwall PL12 6SD
Tel: 01579 351351

Restaurant Menu, Accommodation, No Smoking Area,
Disabled Facilities

44 The Swingletree

202 Launceston Rd, Kelly Bray, Callington,
Cornwall PL17 8DU
Tel: 01579 382395

Real Ales, Bar Food, No Smoking Area

45 Tavistock Arms Hotel

Fore Street, Gunnislake, Cornwall PL18 9BN
Tel: 01822 832217

Real Ales, Bar Food, Restaurant Menu,
No Smoking Area

46 Villages Inn

Rosecraddoc Holiday Village, Liskeard,
Cornwall PL14 5BU
Tel: 01579 347494

Real Ales, Bar Food, Restaurant Menu,
Accommodation, No Smoking Area, Disabled Facilities

47 Weary Friary Inn

Pillaton, Saltash, Cornwall PL12 6QS
Tel: 01579 350238

Real Ales, Bar Food, Restaurant Menu,
Accommodation, No Smoking Area, Disabled Facilities

53 The White Horse

14 Newport Square, Launceston,
Cornwall PL15 8EL
☎ 01566 772084
⊕ www.whitehorselaunceston.co.uk

Real Ales, Bar Food, Restaurant Menu, Accommodation, No Smoking Area, Disabled Facilities

☛ In the Newport area of Launceston, where the A388 turns a sharp corner
🍺 Three rotating brews
🍴 12-2 & 6-9
🛏 4 rooms, 1 en suite
🎵 Live music Fri & Sat eves
🚗 Car park, patio
💳 All the major cards
🕐 11-11
🏛 All the attractions of Launceston

Situated on a corner site in the Newport area of Launceston, the White Horse Inn was built as a farmhouse in 1690. It became an inn in 1714, since when it has had an unbroken history of hospitality. The inn is open all day for drinks, which include three regularly changing real ales to enjoy in the relaxing atmosphere of the bar. The White Horse has built up an enviable reputation for the quality of its cooking, and the menu and specials board offer an impressive choice of cooked-to-order dishes. Booking is recommended at all times, and essential for the traditional Sunday lunch. The inn is an ideal base for exploring the town and the surroundings, with B&B accommodation in four well-appointed rooms; self-catering cottages are also available.

48 Westgate Inn
Westgate Street, Launceston, Cornwall PL15 7AD
Tel: 01566 772493
Real Ales, Bar Food, No Smoking Area

49 Wheal Tor Country Inn and Hotel
Caradon Hill, Pensilva, Nr Liskeard,
Cornwall PL14 5PJ
Tel: 01579 362281
Real Ales, Bar Food, Restaurant Menu,
Accommodation, No Smoking Area, Disabled Facilities

50 The White Hart Hotel
15 Broad St, Launceston, Cornwall PL15 8AL
Tel: 01566 772013
Real Ales, Bar Food, Restaurant Menu,
Accommodation, No Smoking Area, Disabled Facilities

51 White Hart Inn
Chilsworthy, Gunnislake, Cornwall PL18 9PB
Tel: 01822 832307
Real Ales, Bar Food, Restaurant Menu,
No Smoking Area

52 White Horse Inn
The Parade, Liskeard, Cornwall PL14 6AF
Tel: 01579 345954
Real Ales, Bar Food, No Smoking Area

53 **White Horse Inn**
14 Newport Square, Launceston,
Cornwall PL15 8EL
Tel: 01566 772084
Real Ales, Bar Food, Restaurant Menu,
Accommodation, No Smoking Area, Disabled Facilities

See panel opposite

54 **Who'd Have Thought It**
St Dominick, Saltash, Cornwall PL12 6TG
Tel: 01579 350214
Real Ales, Bar Food, Restaurant Menu,
No Smoking Area, Disabled Facilities

55 The Wilsey Down Hotel
Hallworthy, Camelford, Cornwall PL32 9SH
Tel: 01840 261205
Real Ales, Bar Food, Restaurant Menu,
Accommodation, No Smoking Area

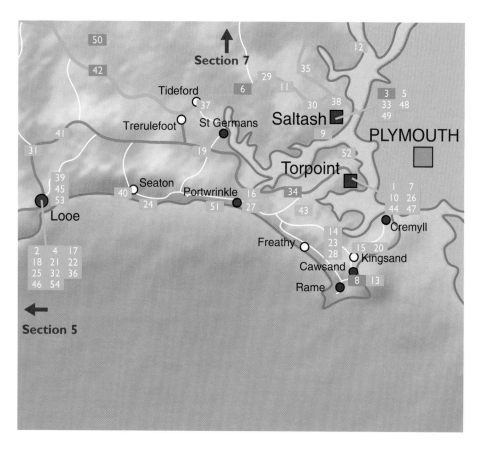

50
42
Section 7
Tideford 6 11
37 29 35
Trerulefoot St Germans Saltash 30 38 3 5
41 33 48
49
31 19 9 PLYMOUTH
52
39 Torpoint
45 Seaton
53 40 Portwrinkle 16 34 1 7
24 51 27 43 10 26
Looe 44 47
14 Cremyll
Freathy 23
2 4 17 28 15 20
18 21 22 Cawsand Kingsand
25 32 36 8 13
46 54 Rame

11   Pub or Inn Reference Number - Detailed Information

12   Pub or Inn Reference Number - Summary Entry

● ■   Place of interest mentioned in the chapter introduction

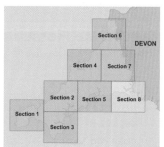

Section 6

DEVON

Section 4   Section 7

Section 2   Section 5   Section 8

Section 1

Section 3

SOUTH EAST CORNWALL

Saltash is the main link between Devon and Cornwall for both rail and road travellers, and there are also ferry connections between the two counties. Attractions in this region include two grand country estates, Antony House and Mount Edgcumbe House.

Cawsand

Before the Plymouth Breakwater was completed in 1841, the Royal Navy fleet used to shelter in Cawsand Bay. The breakwater took 30 years to build, using local limestone; beacon lights are set at either end, almost a mile apart.

Cremyll

The main attraction in the vicinity of this village, which is linked to Plymouth by a passenger ferry, is **Mount Edgcumbe House**. The contents of this superb house include paintings by Sir Joshua Reynolds, Irish horns dating from the Bronze Age, 16th century tapestries and collections of 18th century Plymouth and Chinese porcelain. Both the house and the magnificent gardens are well worth a visit.

Looe

Originally two separate settlements called East Looe and West Looe, linked by a seven-arched bridge built in 1853. Looe is Cornwall's second most important fishing port, with auctions regularly held at East Looe's bustling quayside market. Nearby is Looe's famous stone-built **Banjo Pier**, which takes its name from its shape. Half a mile offshore lies **Looe Island**, one a

sanctuary for smugglers and pirates, now a haven for seabirds, notably shags and cormorants.

Portwrinkle

A small seaside village that developed from its medieval harbour. Now a tiny holiday resort, it has two sand-and-shingle beaches with rock pools. To the east, a signpost points towards Tregantle Fort, built between 1858 and 1868 as part of Plymouth's enhanced defences.

Rame

At the southern end of Whitsand Bay and the southernmost point of **Mount Edgcumbe Country Park**, Rame Head guards the entrance to Plymouth Sound. This beautiful headland has a very special feature – the now ruined 14th century **St Michael's Chapel**, from which a blazing beacon told of the approach of the Spanish Armada. On a clear day Eddystone Lighthouse, ten miles out to sea, can be seen.

Saltash

A small medieval port on the River Tamar, now the main road and rail access point into the county. The wrought-iron **Royal**

Albert Bridge, designed by Isambard Kingdom Brunel, carries the railway, and alongside it the slender **Tamar Bridge**, opened in the early 1960s, handles the considerable quantities of road traffic. Two of the town's most interesting buildings are the **Guildhall**, which stands on granite pillars, and the 15th century **Mary Newman's Cottage**, home of Sir Francis Drake's first wife.

Viaduct at Calstock, near Saltash

St Germans

The **Parish Church** in this quiet rural village stands on the site of a Saxon Cathedral and until the construction of Truro Cathedral in 1910 was the largest church in the county. Features of special interest include a fine west front, two oddly dissimilar towers dating from the 13th and 15th centuries – one octagonal, the other square – and the Burne-Jones east window. Another exceptional building here is the **Sir Willam Moyle's Almshouses**, built in

1583 and restored in 1967.

Torpoint

This delightful small town grew up round the ferry service that began operating across the Tamar Estuary to Devonport in the 18th century. The **Torpoint Ferry** connects the town with Plymouth and provides a convenient alternative to the circuitous journey by road. A mile north of Torpoint stands **Antony House**, a superb 18th century country mansion with a wealth of fine paintings, tapestries and furniture and an idyllic setting in glorious gardens. The adjacent country park takes in a stretch of heritage coastline.

1   Bar Mez

The Old School , Macey Street, Torpoint,
Cornwall PL11 2AJ
Tel: 01752 816844

2   Barbican Inn

Barbican Road, Looe, Cornwall PL13 1EY
Tel: 01503 262746

Real Ales, Bar Food, Disabled Facilities

3   The Boatman

3 Old Ferry Road, Saltash, Cornwall PL12 4EH
Tel: 01752 842099

Real Ales, Bar Food, Restaurant Menu,
No Smoking Area, Disabled Facilities

See panel below

4   Boscarn Hotel

Church End, Looe, Cornwall PL13 1BU
Tel: 01503 262923

Real Ales, Bar Food, Disabled Facilities

5   The Brunel Inn

74-94 Fore Street, Saltash, Cornwall PL12 6AE
Tel: 01752 842261

Real Ales, Bar Food, Accommodation,
No Smoking Area, Disabled Facilities

6   Bullers Arms

The Square, Landrake, Saltash, Cornwall PL12 5DY
Tel: 01752 851283

Real Ales, Bar Food, Restaurant Menu,
No Smoking Area

See panel below

---

3   The Boatman

3 Old Ferry Road, Saltash, Cornwall PL12 4EH
☎ 01752 842099

Real Ales, Bar Food, Restaurant Menu,
No Smoking Area, Disabled Facilities

- In Saltash by the River Tamar, beneath the Tamar road and rail bridges
- 2 rotating ales
- 12-2.30 & 6-9.30 (not Mon eve)
- Major cards except Amex
- Lunchtime and evening
- Torpoint 5 miles, St Mellion 5 miles, Kit Hill 8 miles

The Boatman stands by the river beneath Brunel's wrought-iron railway bridge and the modern road bridge. Behind the pub's smart cream-and-black exterior the bar and restaurant are delightfully traditional. Andy's super cooking is the main attraction, with a fine selection of seafood dishes proving real winners.

6   The Bullers Arms

The Square, Landrake, nr Saltash,
Cornwall PL12 5DY
☎ 01752 851283

Real Ales, Bar Food, Restaurant Menu,
No Smoking Area

- On the A38 4 miles west of Saltash
- Spitfire, Courage Best
- 12-2.30 & 6-9.30
- Live entertainment Sat evening
- Courtyard garden
- Major cards except Amex
- 12-3 & 6-11 (all day in summer)
- Saltash 4 miles

The Bullers Arms, a fine black-and-white building dating from the early 18th century, stands in the shadow of the parish church in the centre of Landrake, three miles west of Saltash. The inn is run by Louise and Dave Vittles and their family, who offer three real ales and a nicely varied menu of home-cooked dishes. The inn has a very pleasant courtyard garden.

8 Cawsand Bay Hotel, Restaurant & Bar

The Bound, Cawsand, Cornwall PL10 1PG

☎ 01752 822425 ⊕ www.cawsandbay.co.uk

Real Ales, Bar Food, Restaurant Menu,
Accommodation, No Smoking Area

- ☞ Cawsand lies 5 miles S of Saltash off the B3247
- 🍺 Sharps Doom Bar, Skinners Tribute
- 🍴 12-2pm & 7pm-9pm
- 🛏 10 en suite rooms
- 🏖 Gardens, car park, private beach
- 💳 Major cards accepted
- 🕐 Open all day
- 🏛 Penlee Point 1 mile, Mount Edgcumbe 2 miles, Torpoint 2 miles, Antony NT 3 miles

Cawsand, an unspoilt fishing village near Penlee Point, was once a notorious haunt of smugglers but is now better known for the Cawsand Bay Hotel, one of the finest in the region. It has one of the best locations of nay hotel in England – right on its own sandy beach

on Cawsand Bay, with stunning views out over the ocean from many of the windows.

Owner Simon Rolfe's outstanding hotel has ten guest bedrooms, all fully en suite, spacious and comfortable, including family rooms accommodating up to six. Two twin rooms are on the ground floor, just a step away from the sand, and all rooms have television, central heating and tea/coffee-making facilities. Special reductions are available for children sharing the family rooms, and the hotel also offers out-of-season deals.

The hotel is fully licensed, and a full range of real ales, beers, lagers, cider, wines, spirits and soft drinks is always available; the newly created ground-level beach bar, like the other amenities, is open all year round. The hotel has earned a great reputation for the standard of its cuisine, and excellent food from the full menu is served every evening and Sunday lunch in the recently refurbished restaurant that looks out over the Bay to Plymouth. The head chef and his staff set great store by the finest and freshest local produce in tried and tested favourites such as prawns Marie Rose, creamy garlic mushrooms, grilled lemon sole, Cornish seafood platter, duck with cherry sauce and steaks prepared in a variety of ways. Some dishes have a more exotic inspiration (halibut served on a bed of Chinese-style noodles) and alternatives include light snacks and bistro-style meals. Booking is recommended for all meals in summer and on Friday and Saturday evening and Sunday lunch throughout the year.

All the amenities of Plymouth are within easy reach using the Torpoint Ferry or Tamar Bridge, and the South West Coast Path runs right behind the hotel.

7 Carbeile Inn

Trevol Road, Torpoint, Cornwall PL11 2NJ
Tel: 01752 814102

Real Ales, Bar Food, Restaurant Menu,
Accommodation, No Smoking Area, Disabled Facilities

8 **Cawsand Bay Hotel**

The Bound, Cawsand, Cornwall PL10 1PG
Tel: 01752 822425

Real Ales, Bar Food, Restaurant Menu,
Accommodation, No Smoking Area

See panel opposite

9 Cecil Arms

St Stevens, Saltash, Cornwall PL12 4AR
Tel: 01752 843408

Real Ales, Bar Food, Restaurant Menu

10 Copley Arms

Hessenford, Torpoint, Cornwall PL11 3HJ
Tel: 01503 240209

Real Ales, Bar Food, Restaurant Menu,
Accommodation, No Smoking Area, Disabled Facilities

11 Crooked Inn

Stoketon Cross, Trematon, Saltash, Cornwall PL12 4RZ
Tel: 01752 848177

Real Ales, Bar Food, Accommodation,
No Smoking Area, Disabled Facilities

12 Crooked Spaniards Inn

Cargreen, Cornwall PL12 6PA
Tel: 01752 842830

Real Ales, Bar Food, Restaurant Menu,
No Smoking Area, Disabled Facilities

13 Cross Keys

The Square, Cawsand, Cornwall PL10 1PF
Tel: 01752 822309

Real Ales, Bar Food, Restaurant Menu,
Accommodation, No Smoking Area, Disabled Facilities

14 Devon and Cornwall Inn

West St, Millbrook, Torpoint, Cornwall PL10 1AA
Tel: 01752 822320

Real Ales, Bar Food, Restaurant Menu,
Accommodation, No Smoking Area

15 Devonport Inn

The Cleave, Kingsand, Cornwall PL10 1NF
Tel: 01752 822869

Real Ales, Bar Food, No Smoking Area

16 Finnygook Inn

Crafthole, Torpoint, Cornwall PL11 3BQ
Tel: 01503 230338

Real Ales, Bar Food, Restaurant Menu,
Accommodation, No Smoking Area, Disabled Facilities

17 The Globe Inn

Station Rd, Looe, Cornwall PL13 1HN
Tel: 01503 262495

Real Ales, Bar Food, Restaurant Menu,
No Smoking Area, Disabled Facilities

18 The Gulls Hotel

Hannafore Road, Looe, Cornwall PL13 2DE
Tel: 01503 262531

Real Ales, Bar Food, Restaurant Menu,
Accommodation

19 Halfway House

Polbathic, Torpoint, Cornwall PL11 3EY
Tel: 01503 230202

Real Ales, Bar Food, Restaurant Menu,
Accommodation, No Smoking Area, Disabled Facilities

20 Halfway House Inn

Fore Street, Kingsand, Torpoint,
Cornwall PL10 1NA
Tel: 01752 822279

Real Ales, Bar Food, Restaurant Menu,
No Smoking Area

21 Hannafore Point Hotel

Marine Drive, West Looe, Cornwall PL13 2DG
Tel: 01503 263273

Real Ales, Bar Food, Restaurant Menu,
Accommodation, No Smoking Area

22 Harbour Moon Inn

Quay Road, West Looe, Cornwall PL13 2BU
Tel: 01503 262873

Real Ales, Bar Food, Restaurant Menu,
Accommodation, No Smoking Area, Disabled Facilities

23 The Heart and Hound
66 West Street Gardens, Millbrook, Torpoint,
Cornwall PL10 1AE
Tel: 01752 822506

24 Inn On The Shore
Down Derry, Torpoint, Cornwall PL11 3JY
Tel: 01503 250210

Real Ales, Bar Food, Restaurant Menu,
Accommodation, No Smoking Area

25 Jolly Sailor Inn
Princes Square, Looe, Cornwall PL13 2EP
Tel: 01503 263387

Real Ales, Bar Food, No Smoking Area

26 The Jubilee
Fore Street, Torpoint, Cornwall PL11 2AD
Tel: 01752 812246

27 The Liscawn Inn
Crafthole, Torpoint, Cornwall PL11 3BD
Tel: 01503 230863

Real Ales, Bar Food, Accommodation,
Disabled Facilities

28 Mark of Friendship
5 New Street, Millbrook, Torpoint,
Cornwall PL10 1BY
Tel: 01752 822253

Real Ales, Bar Food, Accommodation

29 The Notter Bridge
Saltash, Cornwall PL12 4RW
Tel: 01752 842259

Real Ales, Bar Food, Restaurant Menu,
No Smoking Area

30 Ploughboy Inn
Liskeard Road, Saltash, Cornwall PL12 4HG
Tel: 01752 842861

Real Ales, Bar Food, Restaurant Menu,
No Smoking Area, Disabled Facilities

31 Polraen House Hotel
Sandplace, Looe, Cornwall PL13 1PJ
Tel: 01503 263956

Real Ales, Restaurant Menu, Accommodation,
No Smoking Area, Disabled Facilities

32 Portbyhan Hotel
The Quay, West Looe, Looe, Cornwall PL13 2BU
Tel: 01503 262071

Real Ales, Bar Food, Restaurant Menu,
Accommodation, No Smoking Area, Disabled Facilities

33 The Railway Hotel
1 Fore St, Saltash, Cornwall PL12 6AF
Tel: 01752 843691

Real Ales, Bar Food, Accommodation

34 Ring O'Bells
Antony, Torpoint, Cornwall PL11 3AB
Tel: 01752 812572

Real Ales, Bar Food, Restaurant Menu,
Accommodation, No Smoking Area, Disabled Facilities

See panel opposite

35 Rising Sun
Botus Fleming, Cornwall PL12 6NJ
Tel: 01752 842792

Real Ales, Disabled Facilities

36 Rivercroft Hotel
Station Road, Looe, Cornwall PL13 1HL
Tel: 01503 262251

Bar Food, Restaurant Menu, Accommodation,
No Smoking Area

37 Rod and Line Inn
Church Road, Tideford, Saltash,
Cornwall PL12 5HW
Tel: 01752 851323

Real Ales, Bar Food, Restaurant Menu,
No Smoking Area, Disabled Facilities

38 The Rodney
375 New Rd, Saltash, Cornwall PL12 6HL
Tel: 01752 848507

Real Ales

34 The Ring o' Bells

Antony, nr Torpoint, Cornwall PL11 3AB
☎ 01752 812572

Real Ales, Bar Food, Restaurant Menu, Accommodation, No Smoking Area, Disabled Facilities

 On the main A357 from Torpoint Ferry

 Sharps Doom Bar, Bass

 12-9

 4 upstairs rooms

 Quiz, fancy dress & other theme nights

 Small car park

All major cards

① 12-11

 Coastal walks, River Tamar, Antony House 1 mile, Torpoint 2 miles, Plymouth 2 miles by ferry

Easy to spot on the main A387 from Torpoint Ferry, the Ring o' Bells is open all day for drinks and from 12 o'clock to 9 for food. There's plenty of variety on the regular menu and specials board, and traditional roasts add to the options on Sunday.

This is a very sociable place, with quiz, fancy dress and other themed nights throughout the year, and for guests staying overnight the inn has four good-sized upstairs bedrooms. There's plenty to see and do in the area, including Antony House, a superb early 18th century country mansion in the care of the National Trust.

The leaseholders of the Ring o' Bells, Sue and Peter Hartley, also run the village shop.

39 Ship Inn

Fore Street, East Looe, Cornwall PL13 1AD
Tel: 01503 263124

Real Ales, Bar Food, Restaurant Menu, Accommodation, No Smoking Area, Disabled Facilities

40 Smugglers Inn

Tregunnick Lane, Seaton, Looe, Cornwall PL11 3JD
Tel: 01503 250646

Real Ales, Bar Food, Restaurant Menu, Accommodation, No Smoking Area, Disabled Facilities

41 Snooty Fox

Morval, Looe, Cornwall PL13 1PR
Tel: 01503 240233

Real Ales, Bar Food, Restaurant Menu, Accommodation, No Smoking Area, Disabled Facilities

42 Sportsmans Arms Hotel

Lower Clicker Road, Menheniot, Liskeard, Cornwall PL14 3PJ
Tel: 01503 240249

Real Ales, Bar Food, Restaurant Menu, Accommodation, No Smoking Area, Disabled Facilities

See panel on page 110

43 St John Inn

St John, Torpoint, Cornwall PL11 3AW
Tel: 01752 822280

Real Ales, Bar Food, No Smoking Area, Disabled Facilities

44 The Standard Inn

10 Fore St, Torpoint, Cornwall PL11 2AB
Tel: 01752 814252

Real Ales, Bar Food, Restaurant Menu, Accommodation, No Smoking Area, Disabled Facilities

42 The Sportsmans Arms Hotel

Lower Clicker Road, Menheniot, nr Liskeard, Cornwall PL14 3PJ
☎ 01503 240249

Real Ales, Bar Food, Restaurant Menu, Accommodation, No Smoking Area, Disabled Facilities

☛ 1 mile off the A38 2 miles southeast of Liskeard

🍺 Sharp's Doom Bar and others

🍴 Bar and restaurant menus

🛏 7 rooms including a family room

🎵 Live music monthly

⚓ Car park, garden, fishing facilities for residents (2 miles)

💳 Major cards

🕐 12-11

🏛 Residents' fishing 2 miles, Liskeard 3 miles, Looe 6 miles

Just seconds from the A38 and 3 miles from Liskeard, the Sportsmans Arms earns high marks for both food and accommodation. The creeper-clad stone building has a pretty bar-lounge, a non-smoking dining area and a panelled room for darts and pool. Mine host Robert Driver has earned the strong support of both local residents and holidaymakers with an outstanding selection of food that includes the finest Cornish produce, and fresh-air thirsts are quenched by Doom Bar and other Sharp's brews. The guest accommodation comprises seven rooms ranging from singles to a family suite. Anglers can book a fishing holiday at the Sportsmans Arms – Robert owns a fishing lake a short drive down the valley.

50 The White Hart Hotel

Menheniot, nr Liskeard, Cornwall PL14 3QZ
☎ 01579 342245

Real Ales, Bar Food, Restaurant Menu, Accommodation, No Smoking Area, Disabled Facilities

☛ 1 mile off the A38 2 miles southeast of Liskeard

🍺 Courage, John Smiths, guests

🍴 Home cooking – evening only

🛏 7 en suite rooms including 2 family rooms

🎵 Live music monthly

⚓ Car park

💳 Major cards

🕐 12-2.30 & 5-11, all day Fri, Sat & Sun

🏛 Liskeard 3 miles, Looe 6 miles

The White Hart is a fine old hostelry with an unbroken tradition of hospitality going back to the 17th century. The long white-painted frontage is adorned with flowers in spring and summer, and the interior is always warm and inviting. Host Jonathan Thomas welcomes all visitors, whether they've come for a drink, a relaxing evening meal or an overnight or few days' stay.

Local produce is the fore among the home-cooked dishes, which include classics such as cod, scampi, gammon & eggs and superb steaks. Food is served every evening between 7 o'clock and 9. The seven guest bedrooms include two that are ideal for families. The White Hart hosts monthly music evenings featuring local bands.

45 ## Swan Inn

Fore St, East Looe, Looe, Cornwall PL13 1DT
Tel: 01503 263002

Real Ales, Bar Food, Restaurant Menu,
No Smoking Area, Disabled Facilities

---

46 ## Tom Sawyers Tavern

Marine Drive, Looe, Cornwall PL13 2DQ
Tel: 01503 262782

Real Ales, Bar Food, Restaurant Menu,
No Smoking Area

---

47 ## The Trot Inn

11 Fore St, Torpoint, Cornwall PL11 2AB
Tel: 01752 812306

Real Ales

---

48 ## Two Bridges

13 Albert Road, Saltash, Cornwall PL12 4EB
Tel: 01752 848952

Real Ales

---

49 ## The Waterside

Tamar St, Saltash, Cornwall PL12 4EL
Tel: 01752 842266

Real Ales, Bar Food

---

50 ## White Hart Hotel

Menheniot, Liskeard, Cornwall PL14 3QZ
Tel: 01579 342245

Real Ales, Bar Food, Restaurant Menu,
Accommodation, No Smoking Area, Disabled Facilities

See panel opposite

---

51 ## Whitsand Bay Hotel

Portwrinkle, Torpoint, Cornwall PL11 3BU
Tel: 01503 230276

Real Ales, Bar Food, Restaurant Menu,
Accommodation, No Smoking Area, Disabled Facilities

---

52 ## Wilcove Inn

Wilcove, Torpoint, Cornwall PL11 2PG
Tel: 01752 812381

Real Ales, Bar Food, No Smoking Area,
Disabled Facilities

53 ## Ye Old Salutation

Fore St, East Looe, Looe, Cornwall PL13 1AE
Tel: 01503 262784

Real Ales, Bar Food, No Smoking Area

---

54 ## Ye Olde Fishermans Arms

Higher Market Street, Looe, Cornwall PL13 1BW
Tel: 01503 265800

Real Ales

HIDDEN PLACES GUIDES

Explore Britain and Ireland with *Hidden Places* guides - a fascinating series of national and local travel guides.

Packed with easy to read information on hundreds of places of interest as well as places to stay, eat and drink.

Available from both high street and internet booksellers

For more information on the full range of *Hidden Places* guides and other titles published by Travel Publishing visit our website on

www.travelpublishing.co.uk
or ask for our leaflet by phoning **0118-981-7777** or emailing **info@travelpublishing.co.uk**

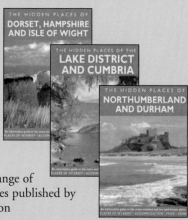

VISIT THE TRAVEL PUBLISHING WEBSITE

Looking for:

- *Places to Visit?*
- *Places to Stay?*
- *Places to Eat & Drink?*
- *Places to Shop?*

Then why not visit the Travel Publishing website...

- Informative pages on places to visit, stay, eat, drink and shop throughout the British Isles.

- Detailed information on Travel Publishing's wide range of national and regional travel guides.

www.travelpublishing.co.uk

TRAVEL PUBLISHING ORDER FORM

To order any of our publications just fill in the payment details below and complete the order form. For orders of less than 4 copies please add £1 per book for postage and packing. Orders over 4 copies are P & P free.

Please Complete Either:

I enclose a cheque for £ [_____] made payable to *Travel Publishing Ltd*

Or:

Card No: [_____] Expiry Date: [_____]

Signature: [_____]

Name: [_____]

Address: [_____]

Tel no: [_____]

Please either send, telephone, fax or e-mail your order to:
Travel Publishing Ltd, 7a Apollo House, Calleva Park, Aldermaston, Berkshire RG7 8TN
Tel: **0118 981 7777**   Fax: **0118 982 0077**   e-mail: info@travelpublishing.co.uk

	Price	Quantity		Price	Quantity
HIDDEN PLACES REGIONAL TITLES			**COUNTRY PUBS AND INNS**		
Cornwall	£8.99	....	Cornwall	£8.99	....
Devon	£8.99	....	Devon	£8.99	....
Dorset, Hants & Isle of Wight	£8.99	....	Sussex	£8.99	....
East Anglia	£8.99	....	Wales	£8.99	....
Lake District & Cumbria	£8.99	....	**COUNTRY LIVING RURAL GUIDES**		
Northumberland & Durham	£8.99	....	East Anglia	£10.99	....
Peak District	£8.99	....	Heart of England	£10.99	....
Sussex	£8.99	....	Ireland	£11.99	....
Yorkshire	£8.99	....	North East	£10.99	....
HIDDEN PLACES NATIONAL TITLES			North West	£10.99	....
England	£11.99	....	Scotland	£11.99	....
Ireland	£11.99	....	South of England	£10.99	....
Scotland	£11.99	....	South East of England	£10.99	....
Wales	£11.99	....	Wales	£11.99	....
HIDDEN INNS TITLES			West Country	£10.99	....
East Anglia	£7.99	....	**OTHER TITLES**		
Heart of England	£7.99	....	Off the Motorway	£11.99	....
North of England	£7.99	....			
South	£7.99	....			
South East	£7.99	....	**Total Quantity:**	[_____]	
Wales	£7.99	....			
West Country	£7.99	....	**Post & Packing:**	[_____]	
Yorkshire	£7.99	....			
			Total Value:	[_____]	

Reader Reaction Form

The *Travel Publishing* research team would like to receive reader's comments on any pubs and inns covered (or not covered) in this guide so please do not hesitate to write to us using these reader reaction forms. We would also welcome recommendations for suitable entries to be included in the next edition. This will help ensure that the *Country Pubs and Inns series of Guides* continues to provide a comprehensive list of pubs and inns to our readers. To provide your comments or recommendations would you please complete the forms below and overleaf as indicated and send to:

The Research Department, Travel Publishing Ltd,
7a Apollo House, Calleva Park, Aldermaston, Reading, RG7 8TN.

Your Name:

Your Address:

Your Telephone Number:

Please tick as appropriate:

Comments ☐   Recommendation ☐

Name of Establishment:

Address:

Telephone Number:

Name of Contact:

Reader Reaction Form

Comment or Reason for Recommendation:

....
....
....
....
....
....
....
....
....
....
....
....
....
....
....
....
....
....
....
....

Reader Reaction Form

The *Travel Publishing* research team would like to receive reader's comments on any pubs and inns covered (or not covered) in this guide so please do not hesitate to write to us using these reader reaction forms. We would also welcome recommendations for suitable entries to be included in the next edition. This will help ensure that the *Country Pubs and Inns series of Guides* continues to provide a comprehensive list of pubs and inns to our readers. To provide your comments or recommendations would you please complete the forms below and overleaf as indicated and send to:

The Research Department, Travel Publishing Ltd,
7a Apollo House, Calleva Park, Aldermaston, Reading, RG7 8TN.

Your Name:

Your Address:

Your Telephone Number:

Please tick as appropriate:

Comments ☐   Recommendation ☐

Name of Establishment:

Address:

Telephone Number:

Name of Contact:

Reader Reaction Form

Comment or Reason for Recommendation:

....

....

....

....

....

....

....

....

....

....

....

....

....

....

....

....

....

....

Reader Reaction Form

The *Travel Publishing* research team would like to receive reader's comments on any pubs and inns covered (or not covered) in this guide so please do not hesitate to write to us using these reader reaction forms. We would also welcome recommendations for suitable entries to be included in the next edition. This will help ensure that the *Country Pubs and Inns series of Guides* continues to provide a comprehensive list of pubs and inns to our readers. To provide your comments or recommendations would you please complete the forms below and overleaf as indicated and send to:

The Research Department, Travel Publishing Ltd,
7a Apollo House, Calleva Park, Aldermaston, Reading, RG7 8TN.

Your Name:

Your Address:

Your Telephone Number:

Please tick as appropriate:

Comments ☐   Recommendation ☐

Name of Establishment:

Address:

Telephone Number:

Name of Contact:

Reader Reaction Form

Comment or Reason for Recommendation:

....

....

....

....

....

....

....

....

....

....

....

....

....

....

....

....

....

....